Kim and the computer stories
Stage 8

Name

Sequence the story.

1   One day Kim was playing a spelling game on the computer.

It was Bleep. 'I can help you to get the mouse working again,' he said.

Kim saw some little footprints. They were mouse prints.

She tried to spell the word **sat** but the mouse made **rat**.

The computer screen went red, then blue, then green and a little face appeared.

'First we must find out where Mouse lives,' said Bleep.

Kim and Bleep followed the prints to a little mouse house.

'Thank you,' said Mouse. 'Now I can get back to work.'

Kim and Bleep gave Mouse a nice warm drink and some cheese.

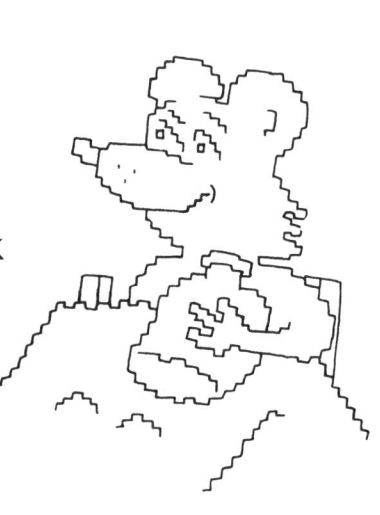

Kim and the computer mouse

Skill: Reading for meaning
Instructions: Read all the sentences, then number them in the correct order.

Circle the blend.

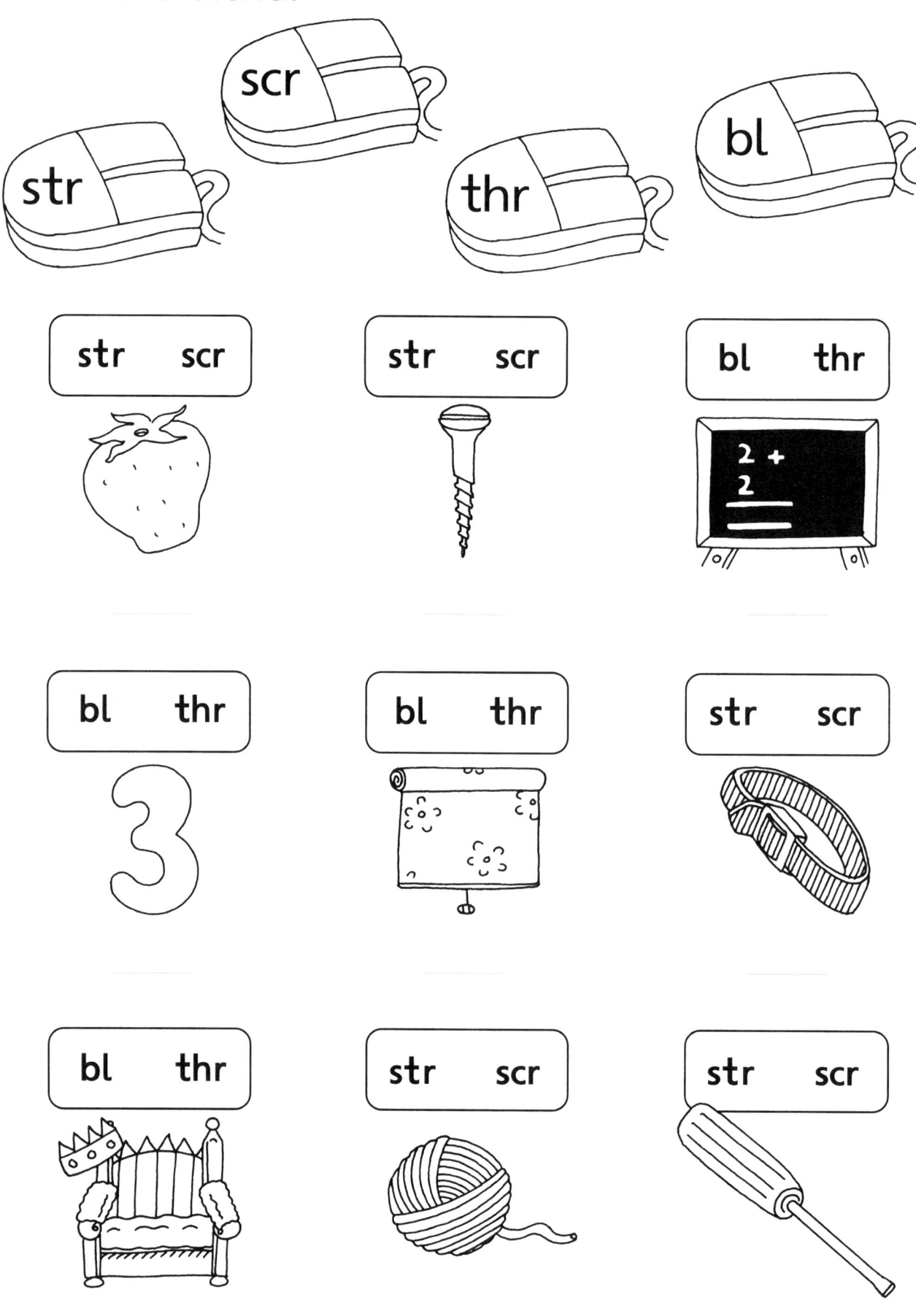

Kim and the computer mouse

Skill: Recognizing blends
Instructions: Circle the correct blend above each picture and then write the blend under the picture.

True or false?

Kim was making up a story about a giant.	true	false
Bleep wanted to see a giant.	true	false
There was no food to eat on the table.	true	false
The giant threw Kim and Bleep down a big hole.	true	false
Kim and Bleep climbed out of the giant's window.	true	false
Kim and Bleep ran across the keyboard.	true	false
The giant jumped on the Delete key and disappeared.	true	false
Kim and Bleep jumped on the Delete key.	true	false
Kim was not hungry at the end of the story.	true	false
When Kim got back into the classroom it was time for lunch.	true	false

Kim and the computer giant

Skill: Story recall and comprehension
Instructions: Read the sentences and decide whether they are true or false. Circle the correct answer. Look back at the story to check your answers.

Match the words.

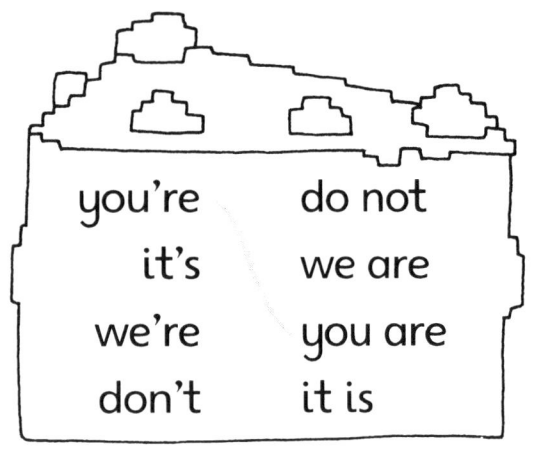

you're — do not
it's — we are
we're — you are
don't — it is

there's — we will
I'm — he is
we'll — there is
he's — I am

Write one word for two words.

        you are

Bleep said, 'If _____ hungry, there's lots of food in here.'

      do not

'I hope we _____ see your hungry giant,' said Bleep.

        It is

'Oh no,' said Bleep. '_____ your hungry giant.'

       We are

'Oh no,' said Kim. '_____ in the giant's cooking pot.'

  We will

'_____ have to climb up the giant vegetables,' said Bleep.

       He is

'Quick,' said Kim. '_____ coming to get us.'

           I am

'We have got away from the giant. But now _____ even more hungry,' said Kim.

Kim and the computer giant

Skill: Using the apostrophe to mark missing letters
Instructions: Join the contraction to the matching two words. Then write the contractions in the sentences.

My own story

Kim   Bleep   Little Red Riding Hood   Paintbrush

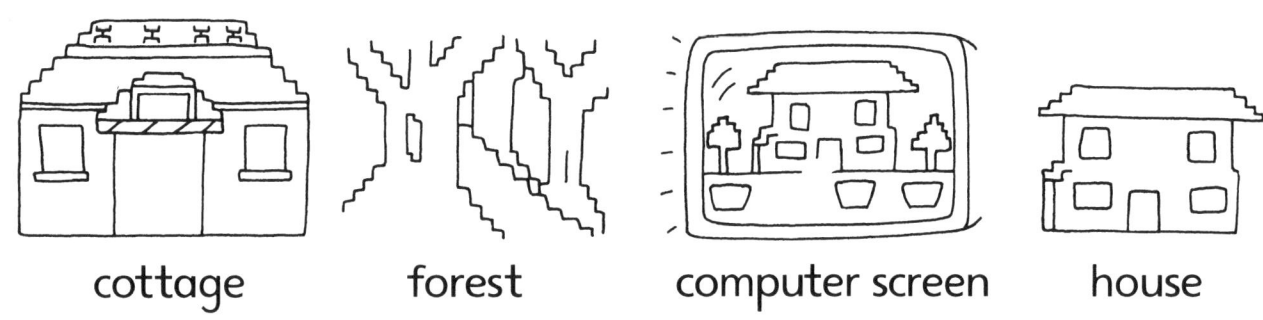

cottage   forest   computer screen   house

Kim and the missing paint pot

Skill: Story writing
Instructions: Choose some characters and an object/setting. Write a new story or re-tell the story of Kim and the missing paint pot.

Answer the questions.

What was Kim making on the computer? (page 2)

Why was Paintbrush cross? (page 5)

What did Cinderella have all over her dress? (page 7)

Who had a beautiful red doll's house? (page 9)

Why had Grandmother taken the red paint? (page 11)

Why did Mrs Morris tell Kim to turn off the computer? (page 15)

Who was painting the roof in Kim's picture? (page 16)

Kim and the missing paint pot

Skill: Comprehension
Instructions: Answer the questions. Look back at the story to help you.

Fill in the gaps.

Kim was playing a shape game on _____ computer.

Bleep said, 'I can help you to _____ the missing triangle.'

Kim and Bleep _____ through the door into a long tunnel.

'The shape dragon has taken all the triangles,' _____ Bleep.

At the back of the cave _____ a dragon.

The dragon had big red triangles _____ his back.

'Please may I _____ one of your triangles?' said Kim.

'I will _____ you my star badge,' said Kim.

So Kim gave the dragon the star badge from _____ jumper.

The dragon gave Kim the little green triangle from the _____ of his tail.

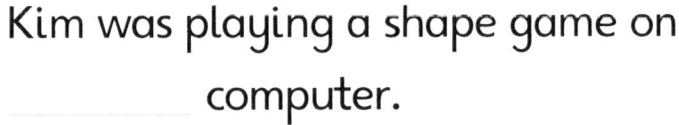

Kim and the shape dragon

Skill: Reading comprehension - cloze
Instructions: Read the sentences carefully and then fill in each gap with a suitable word.

Make the words.

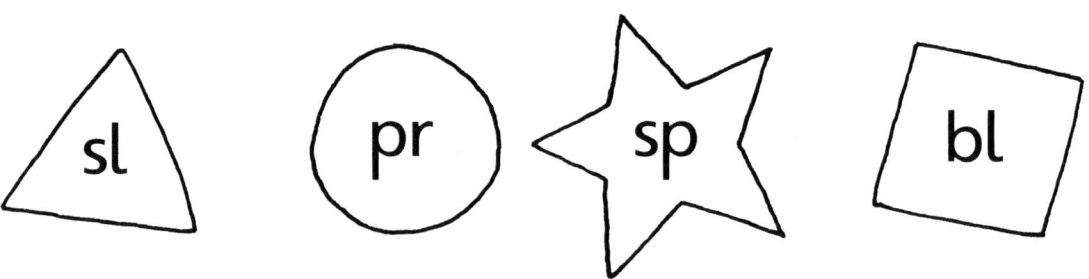

ip
ap
id

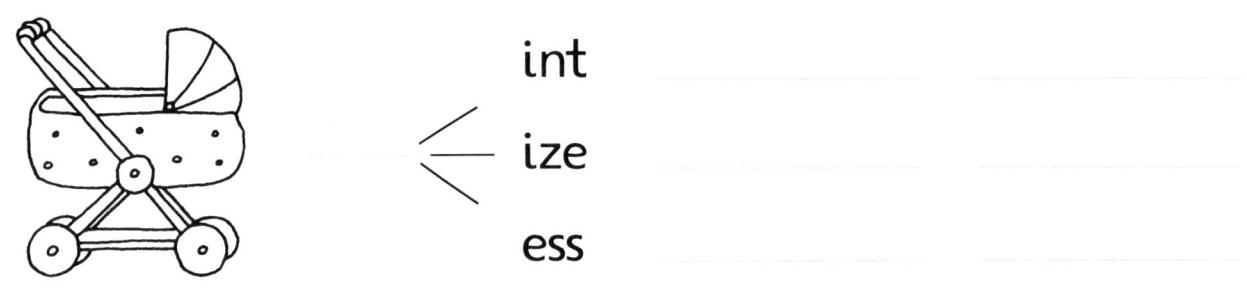

int
ize
ess

ell
ot
in

ack
ink
ock

Kim and the shape dragon

Skill: Recognizing blends and word-building
Instructions: Write the blend next to the picture. Then use the blend and endings to make the words and write the words twice.

Kim and the computer stories
Stage 8

Name

Sequence the story.

1   One day Kim was playing a spelling game on the computer.

It was Bleep. 'I can help you to get the mouse working again,' he said.

Kim saw some little footprints. They were mouse prints.

She tried to spell the word **sat** but the mouse made **rat**.

The computer screen went red, then blue, then green and a little face appeared.

'First we must find out where Mouse lives,' said Bleep.

Kim and Bleep followed the prints to a little mouse house.

'Thank you,' said Mouse. 'Now I can get back to work.'

Kim and Bleep gave Mouse a nice warm drink and some cheese.

Kim and the computer mouse

Skill: Reading for meaning
Instructions: Read all the sentences, then number them in the correct order.

Circle the blend.

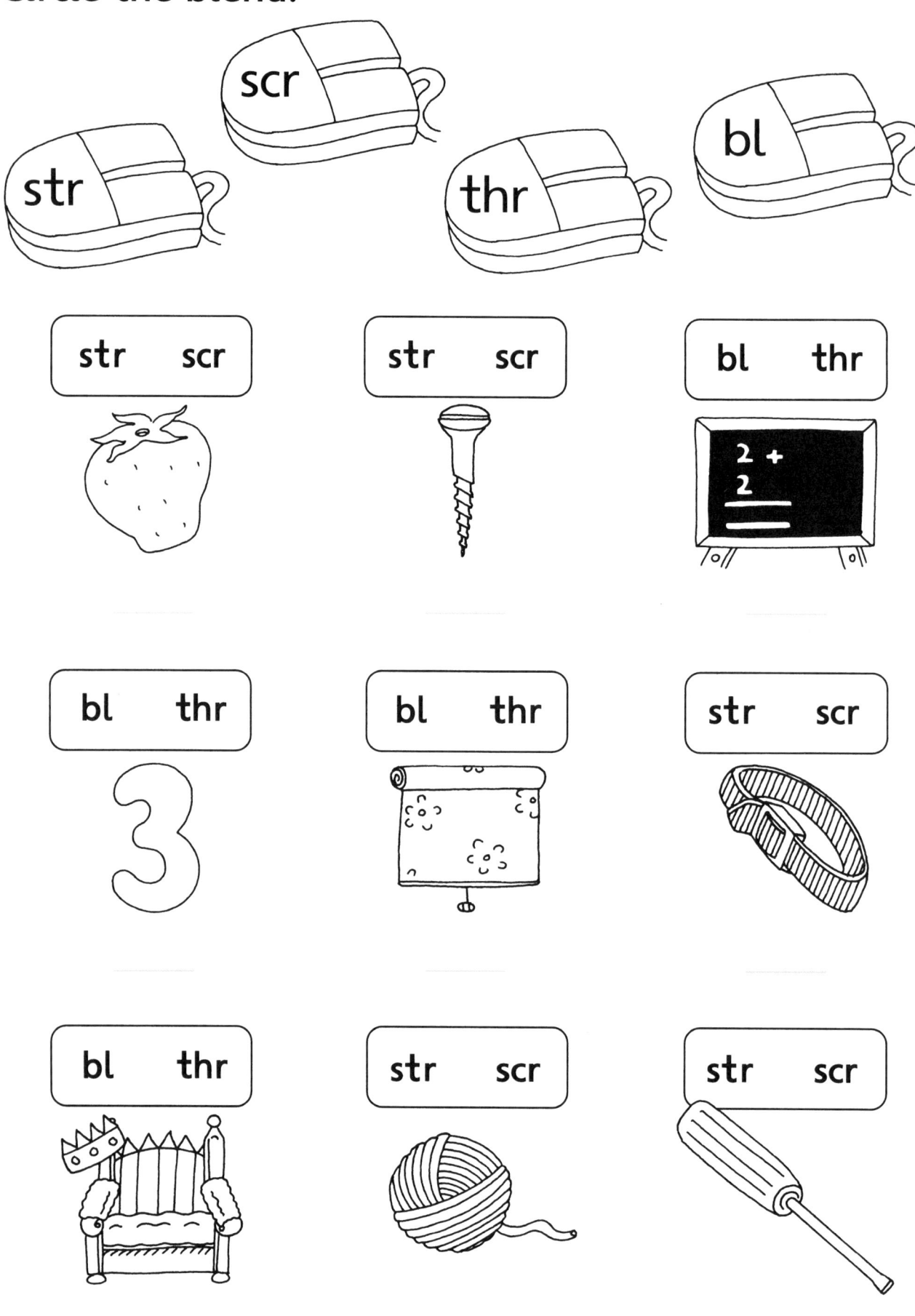

Kim and the computer mouse

Skill: Recognizing blends
Instructions: Circle the correct blend above each picture and then write the blend under the picture.

True or false?

Kim was making up a story about a giant.	true	false
Bleep wanted to see a giant.	true	false
There was no food to eat on the table.	true	false
The giant threw Kim and Bleep down a big hole.	true	false
Kim and Bleep climbed out of the giant's window.	true	false
Kim and Bleep ran across the keyboard.	true	false
The giant jumped on the Delete key and disappeared.	true	false
Kim and Bleep jumped on the Delete key.	true	false
Kim was not hungry at the end of the story.	true	false
When Kim got back into the classroom it was time for lunch.	true	false

Kim and the computer giant

Skill: Story recall and comprehension
Instructions: Read the sentences and decide whether they are true or false. Circle the correct answer. Look back at the story to check your answers.

Match the words.

you're — do not
it's — we are
we're — you are
don't — it is

there's
I'm
we'll
he's
we will
he is
there is
I am

Write one word for two words.

you are

Bleep said, 'If _____ hungry, there's lots of food in here.'

do not

'I hope we _____ see your hungry giant,' said Bleep.

It is

'Oh no,' said Bleep. '_____ your hungry giant.'

We are

'Oh no,' said Kim. '_____ in the giant's cooking pot.'

We will

'_____ have to climb up the giant vegetables,' said Bleep.

He is

'Quick,' said Kim. '_____ coming to get us.'

I am

'We have got away from the giant. But now _____ even more hungry,' said Kim.

Kim and the computer giant

Skill: Using the apostrophe to mark missing letters
Instructions: Join the contraction to the matching two words. Then write the contractions in the sentences.

My own story

Kim   Bleep   Little Red Riding Hood   Paintbrush

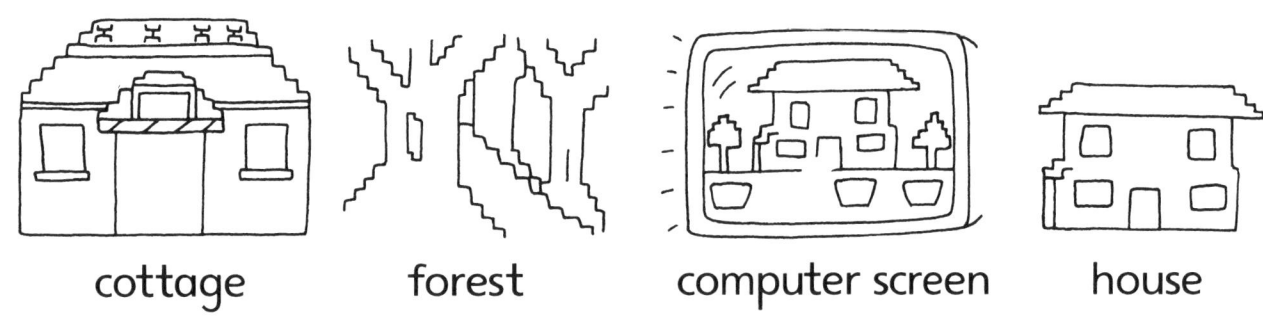

cottage   forest   computer screen   house

Kim and the missing paint pot

Skill: Story writing
Instructions: Choose some characters and an object/setting. Write a new story or re-tell the story of Kim and the missing paint pot.

Answer the questions.

What was Kim making on the computer? (page 2)

Why was Paintbrush cross? (page 5)

What did Cinderella have all over her dress? (page 7)

Who had a beautiful red doll's house? (page 9)

Why had Grandmother taken the red paint? (page 11)

Why did Mrs Morris tell Kim to turn off the computer? (page 15)

Who was painting the roof in Kim's picture? (page 16)

Kim and the missing paint pot

Skill: Comprehension
Instructions: Answer the questions. Look back at the story to help you.

Fill in the gaps.

Kim was playing a shape game on _____ computer.

Bleep said, 'I can help you to _____ the missing triangle.'

Kim and Bleep _____ through the door into a long tunnel.

'The shape dragon has taken all the triangles,' _____ Bleep.

At the back of the cave _____ a dragon.

The dragon had big red triangles _____ his back.

'Please may I _____ one of your triangles?' said Kim.

'I will _____ you my star badge,' said Kim.

So Kim gave the dragon the star badge from _____ jumper.

The dragon gave Kim the little green triangle from the _____ of his tail.

Kim and the shape dragon

Skill: Reading comprehension - cloze
Instructions: Read the sentences carefully and then fill in each gap with a suitable word.

Make the words.

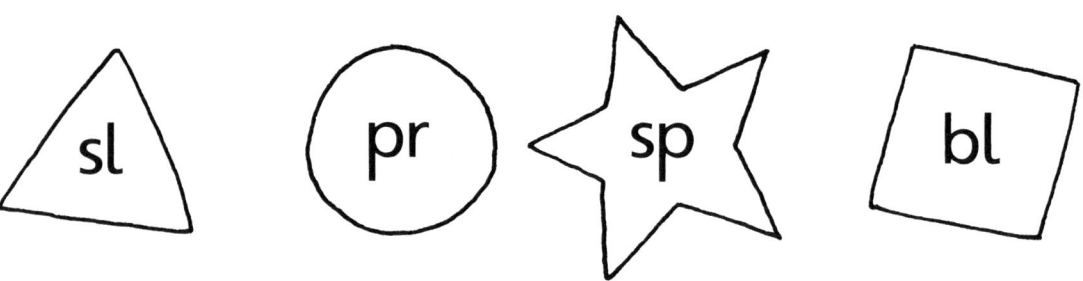

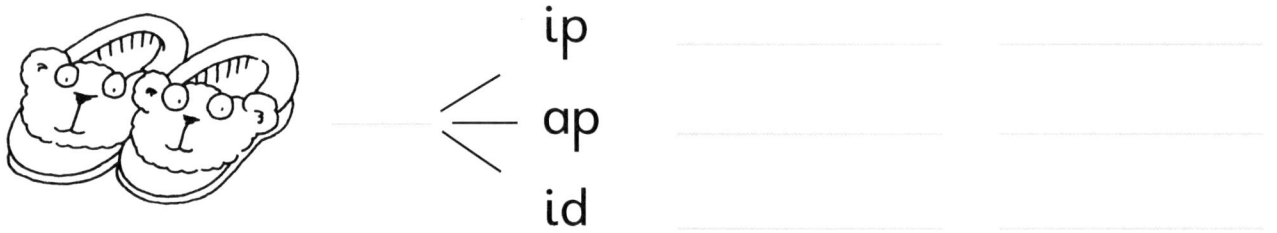

ip
ap
id

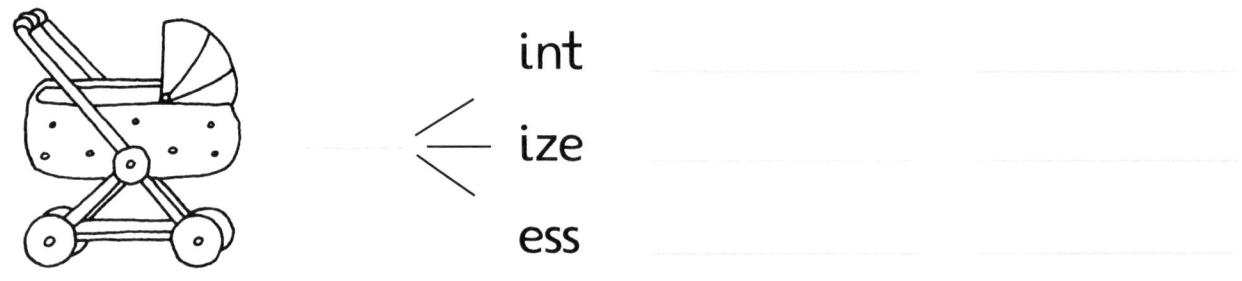

int
ize
ess

ell
ot
in

ack
ink
ock

Kim and the shape dragon

Skill: Recognizing blends and word-building
Instructions: Write the blend next to the picture. Then use the blend and endings to make the words and write the words twice.

Kim and the computer stories
Stage 8

Name

Sequence the story.

1   One day Kim was playing a spelling game on the computer.

It was Bleep. 'I can help you to get the mouse working again,' he said.

Kim saw some little footprints. They were mouse prints.

She tried to spell the word **sat** but the mouse made **rat**.

The computer screen went red, then blue, then green and a little face appeared.

'First we must find out where Mouse lives,' said Bleep.

Kim and Bleep followed the prints to a little mouse house.

'Thank you,' said Mouse. 'Now I can get back to work.'

Kim and Bleep gave Mouse a nice warm drink and some cheese.

Kim and the computer mouse

Skill: Reading for meaning
Instructions: Read all the sentences, then number them in the correct order.

Circle the blend.

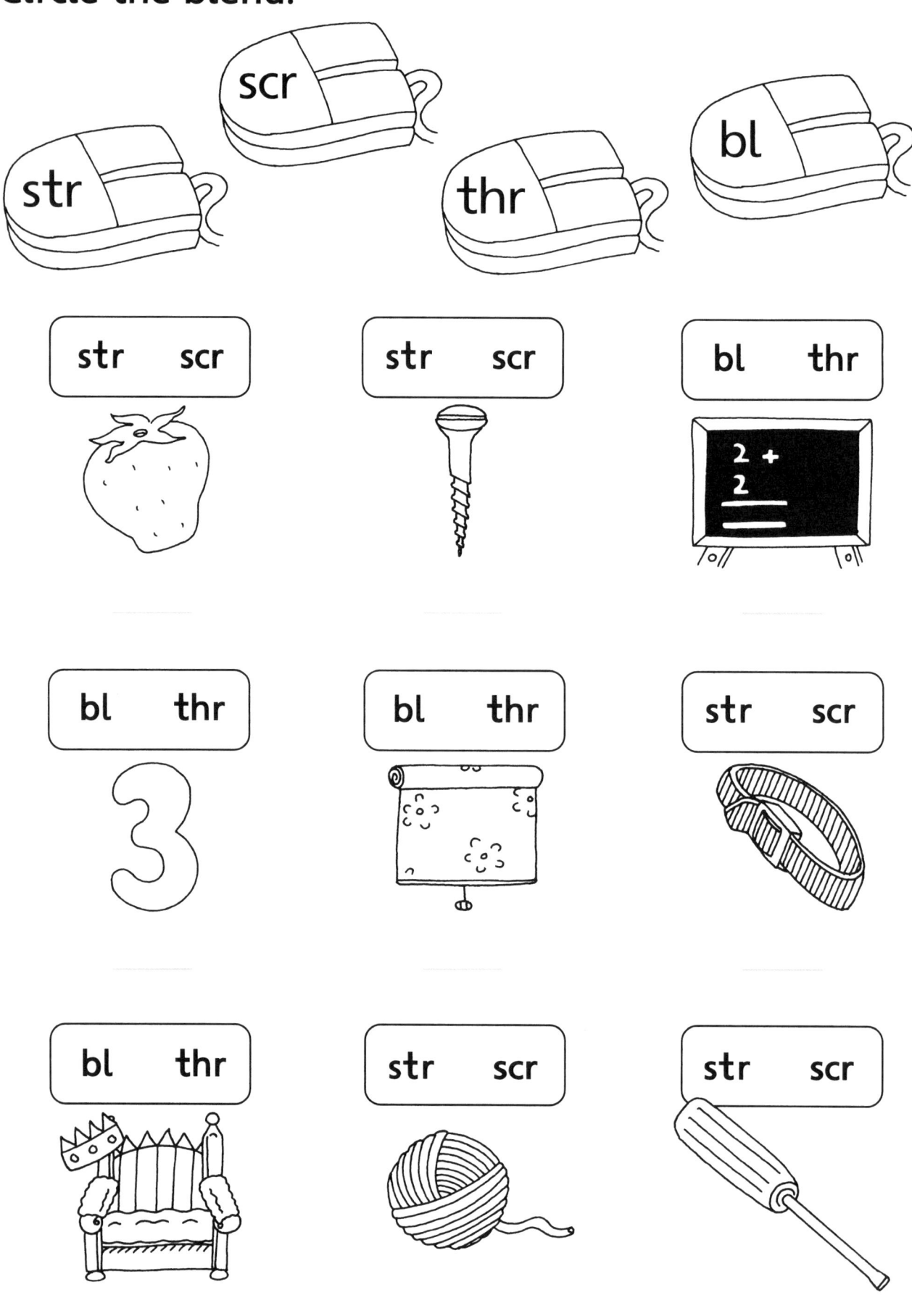

Kim and the computer mouse

Skill: Recognizing blends
Instructions: Circle the correct blend above each picture and then write the blend under the picture.

True or false?

Kim was making up a story about a giant.	true	false
Bleep wanted to see a giant.	true	false
There was no food to eat on the table.	true	false
The giant threw Kim and Bleep down a big hole.	true	false
Kim and Bleep climbed out of the giant's window.	true	false
Kim and Bleep ran across the keyboard.	true	false
The giant jumped on the Delete key and disappeared.	true	false
Kim and Bleep jumped on the Delete key.	true	false
Kim was not hungry at the end of the story.	true	false
When Kim got back into the classroom it was time for lunch.	true	false

Kim and the computer giant

Skill: Story recall and comprehension
Instructions: Read the sentences and decide whether they are true or false. Circle the correct answer. Look back at the story to check your answers.

Match the words.

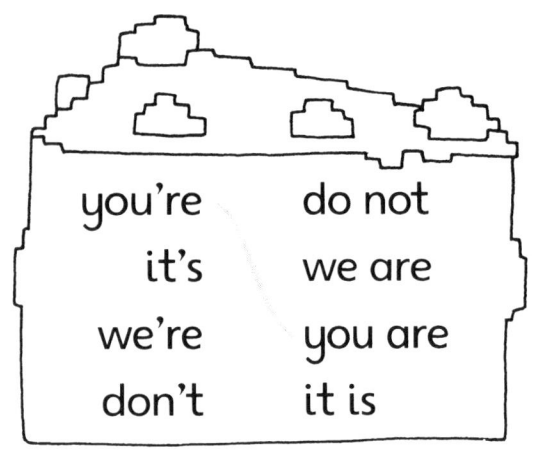

you're — do not
it's — we are
we're — you are
don't — it is

there's — we will
I'm — he is
we'll — there is
he's — I am

Write one word for two words.

you are

Bleep said, 'If _____ hungry, there's lots of food in here.'

do not

'I hope we _____ see your hungry giant,' said Bleep.

It is

'Oh no,' said Bleep. '_____ your hungry giant.'

We are

'Oh no,' said Kim. '_____ in the giant's cooking pot.'

We will

'_____ have to climb up the giant vegetables,' said Bleep.

He is

'Quick,' said Kim. '_____ coming to get us.'

I am

'We have got away from the giant. But now _____ even more hungry,' said Kim.

Kim and the computer giant

Skill: Using the apostrophe to mark missing letters
Instructions: Join the contraction to the matching two words. Then write the contractions in the sentences.

My own story

Kim   Bleep   Little Red Riding Hood   Paintbrush

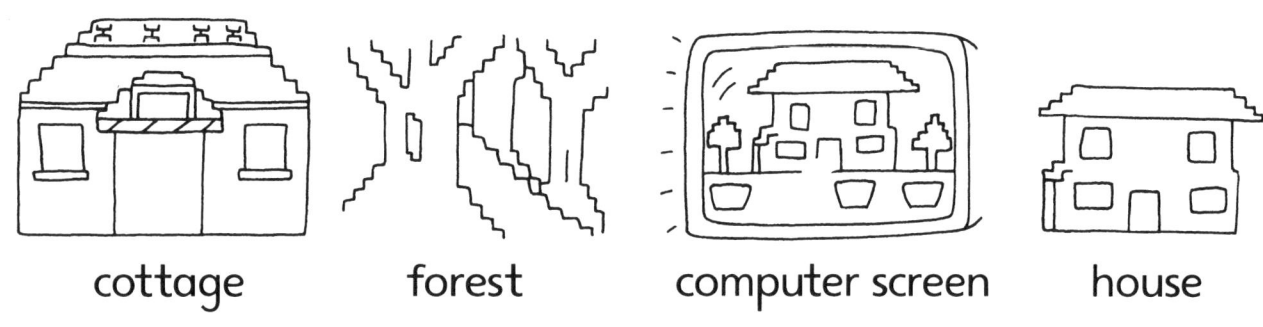

cottage   forest   computer screen   house

Kim and the missing paint pot

Skill: Story writing
Instructions: Choose some characters and an object/setting. Write a new story or re-tell the story of Kim and the missing paint pot.

Answer the questions.

What was Kim making on the computer? (page 2)

Why was Paintbrush cross? (page 5)

What did Cinderella have all over her dress? (page 7)

Who had a beautiful red doll's house? (page 9)

Why had Grandmother taken the red paint? (page 11)

Why did Mrs Morris tell Kim to turn off the computer? (page 15)

Who was painting the roof in Kim's picture? (page 16)

Kim and the missing paint pot

Skill: Comprehension
Instructions: Answer the questions. Look back at the story to help you.

Fill in the gaps.

Kim was playing a shape game on _____ computer.

Bleep said, 'I can help you to _____ the missing triangle.'

Kim and Bleep _____ through the door into a long tunnel.

'The shape dragon has taken all the triangles,' _____ Bleep.

At the back of the cave _____ a dragon.

The dragon had big red triangles _____ his back.

'Please may I _____ one of your triangles?' said Kim.

'I will _____ you my star badge,' said Kim.

So Kim gave the dragon the star badge from _____ jumper.

The dragon gave Kim the little green triangle from the _____ of his tail.

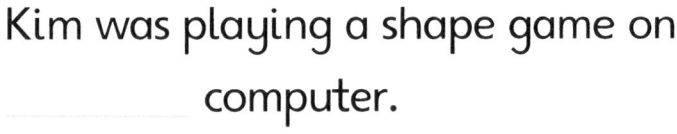

Kim and the shape dragon

Skill: Reading comprehension – cloze
Instructions: Read the sentences carefully and then fill in each gap with a suitable word.

Make the words.

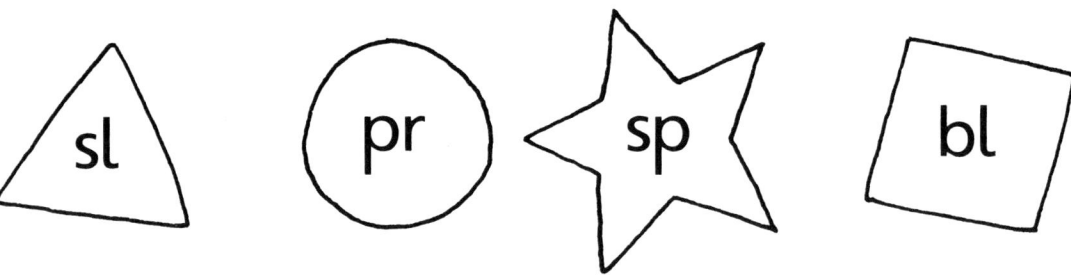

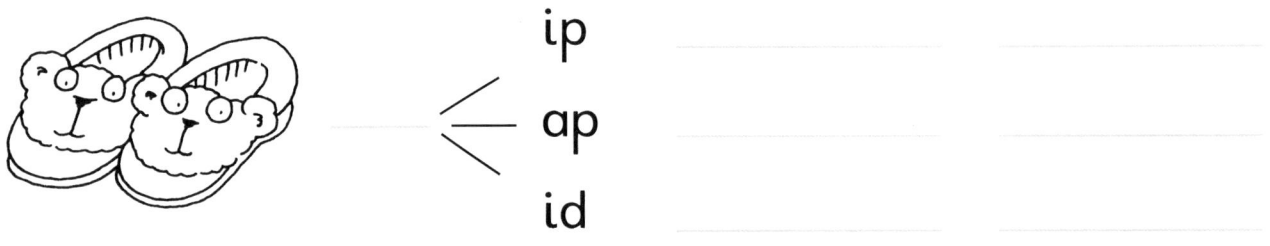

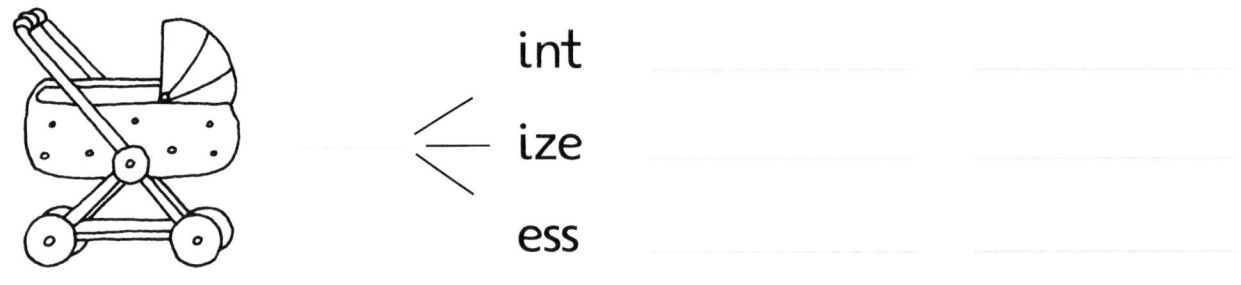

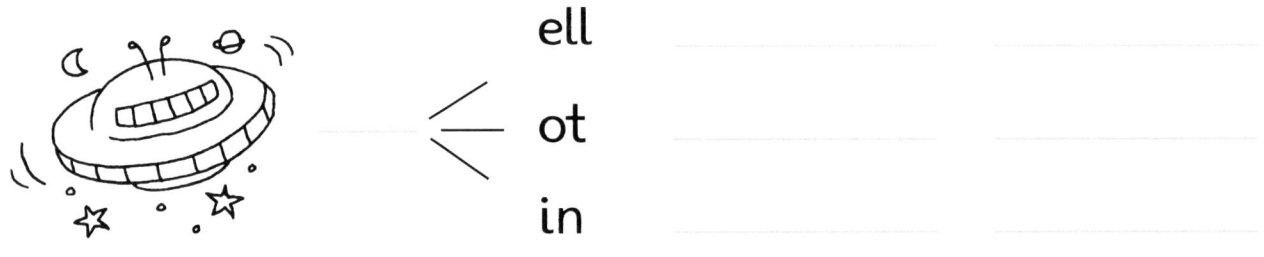

Kim and the shape dragon

Skill: Recognizing blends and word-building
Instructions: Write the blend next to the picture. Then use the blend and endings to make the words and write the words twice.

Kim and the computer stories
Stage 8

Name

Sequence the story.

1   One day Kim was playing a spelling game on the computer.

It was Bleep. 'I can help you to get the mouse working again,' he said.

Kim saw some little footprints. They were mouse prints.

She tried to spell the word **sat** but the mouse made **rat**.

The computer screen went red, then blue, then green and a little face appeared.

'First we must find out where Mouse lives,' said Bleep.

Kim and Bleep followed the prints to a little mouse house.

'Thank you,' said Mouse. 'Now I can get back to work.'

Kim and Bleep gave Mouse a nice warm drink and some cheese.

Kim and the computer mouse

Skill: Reading for meaning
Instructions: Read all the sentences, then number them in the correct order.

Circle the blend.

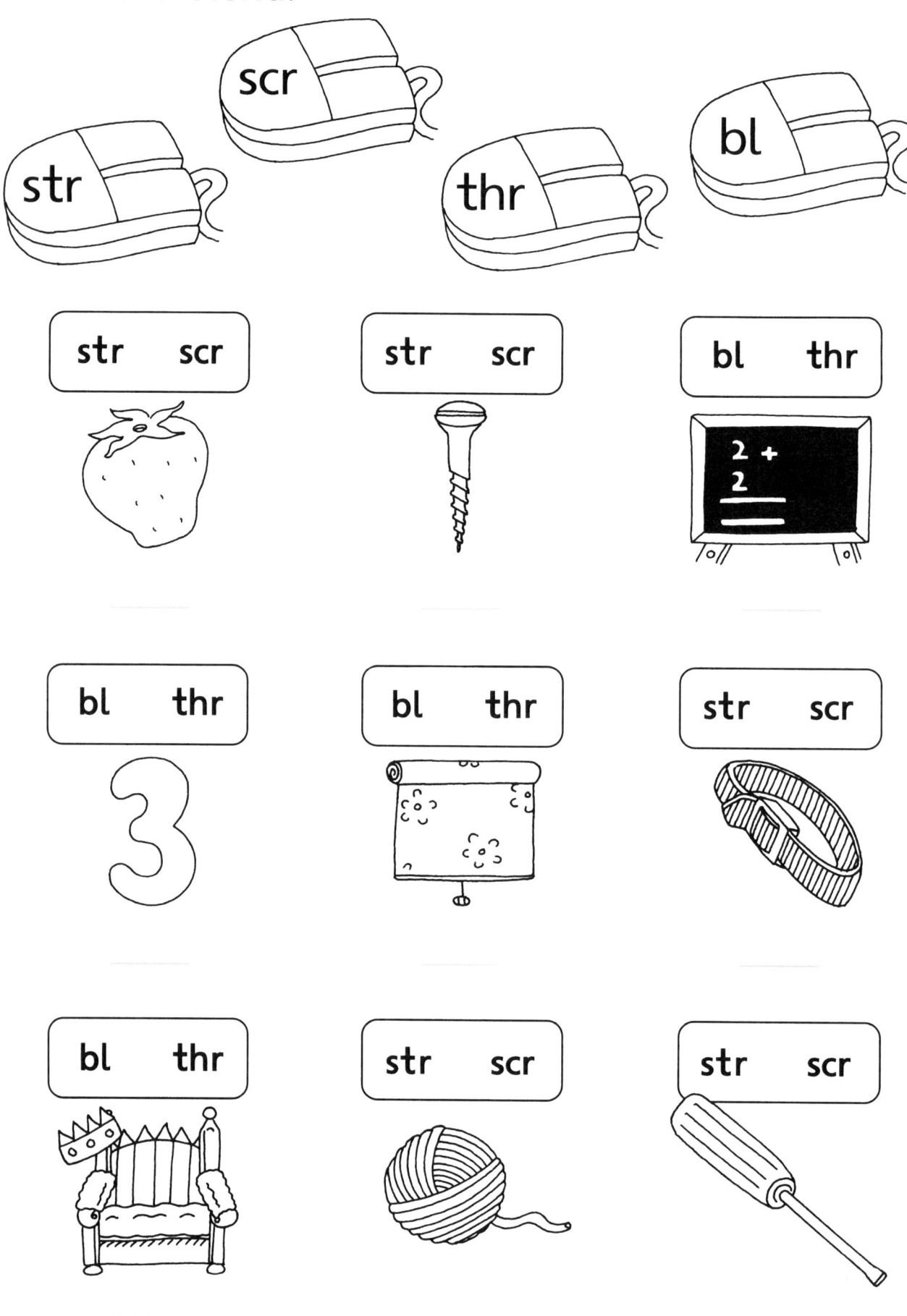

Kim and the computer mouse

Skill: Recognizing blends
Instructions: Circle the correct blend above each picture and then write the blend under the picture.

True or false?

Kim was making up a story about a giant.	true	false
Bleep wanted to see a giant.	true	false
There was no food to eat on the table.	true	false
The giant threw Kim and Bleep down a big hole.	true	false
Kim and Bleep climbed out of the giant's window.	true	false
Kim and Bleep ran across the keyboard.	true	false
The giant jumped on the Delete key and disappeared.	true	false
Kim and Bleep jumped on the Delete key.	true	false
Kim was not hungry at the end of the story.	true	false
When Kim got back into the classroom it was time for lunch.	true	false

Kim and the computer giant

Skill: Story recall and comprehension
Instructions: Read the sentences and decide whether they are true or false. Circle the correct answer. Look back at the story to check your answers.

Match the words.

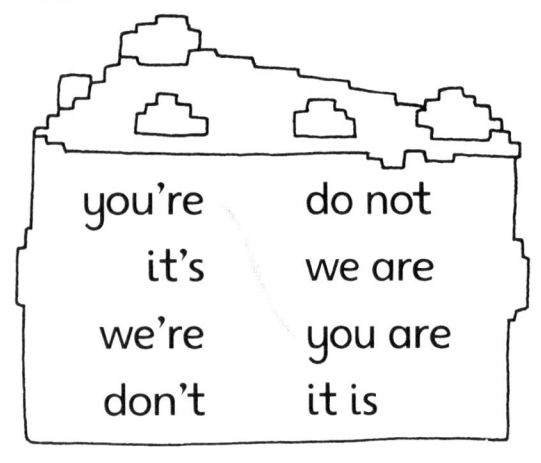

Write one word for two words.

you are

Bleep said, 'If _____ hungry, there's lots of food in here.'

do not

'I hope we _____ see your hungry giant,' said Bleep.

It is

'Oh no,' said Bleep. '_____ your hungry giant.'

We are

'Oh no,' said Kim. '_____ in the giant's cooking pot.'

We will

'_____ have to climb up the giant vegetables,' said Bleep.

He is

'Quick,' said Kim. '_____ coming to get us.'

I am

'We have got away from the giant. But now _____ even more hungry,' said Kim.

Kim and the computer giant

Skill: Using the apostrophe to mark missing letters
Instructions: Join the contraction to the matching two words. Then write the contractions in the sentences.

My own story

Kim   Bleep   Little Red Riding Hood   Paintbrush

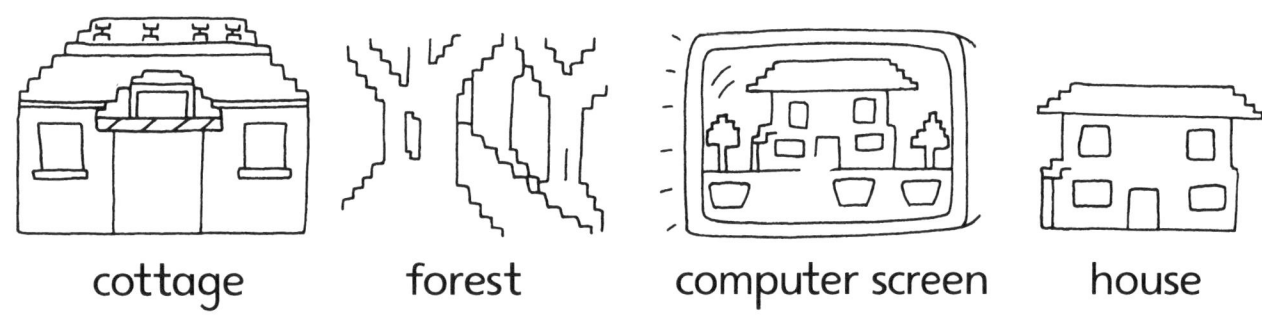

cottage   forest   computer screen   house

Kim and the missing paint pot

Skill: Story writing
Instructions: Choose some characters and an object/setting. Write a new story or re-tell the story of Kim and the missing paint pot.

Answer the questions.

What was Kim making on the computer? (page 2)

Why was Paintbrush cross? (page 5)

What did Cinderella have all over her dress? (page 7)

Who had a beautiful red doll's house? (page 9)

Why had Grandmother taken the red paint? (page 11)

Why did Mrs Morris tell Kim to turn off the computer? (page 15)

Who was painting the roof in Kim's picture? (page 16)

Kim and the missing paint pot

Skill: Comprehension
Instructions: Answer the questions. Look back at the story to help you.

Fill in the gaps.

Kim was playing a shape game on _____ computer.

Bleep said, 'I can help you to _____ the missing triangle.'

Kim and Bleep _____ through the door into a long tunnel.

'The shape dragon has taken all the triangles,' _____ Bleep.

At the back of the cave _____ a dragon.

The dragon had big red triangles _____ his back.

'Please may I _____ one of your triangles?' said Kim.

'I will _____ you my star badge,' said Kim.

So Kim gave the dragon the star badge from _____ jumper.

The dragon gave Kim the little green triangle from the _____ of his tail.

Kim and the shape dragon

Skill: Reading comprehension - cloze
Instructions: Read the sentences carefully and then fill in each gap with a suitable word.

Make the words.

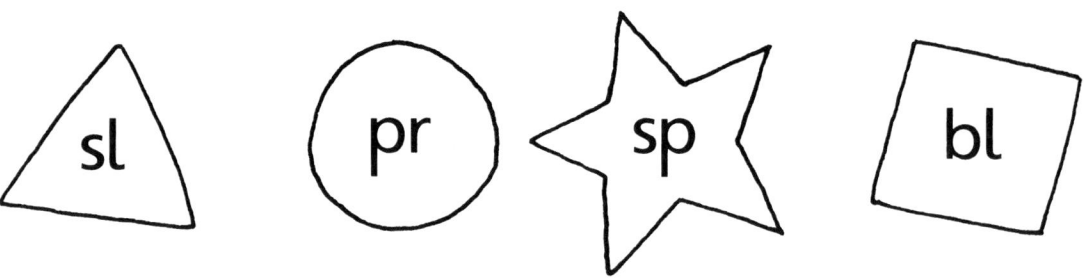

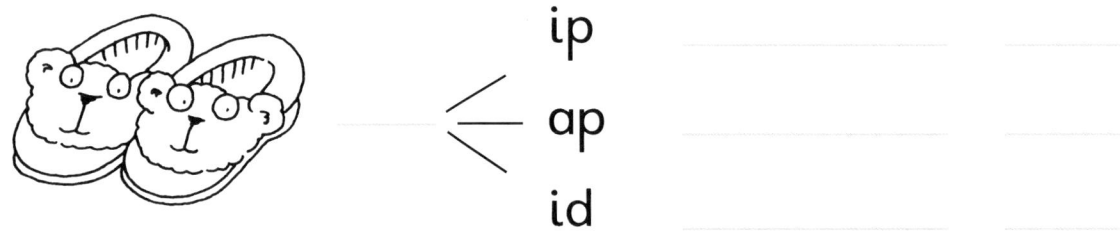

ip
ap
id

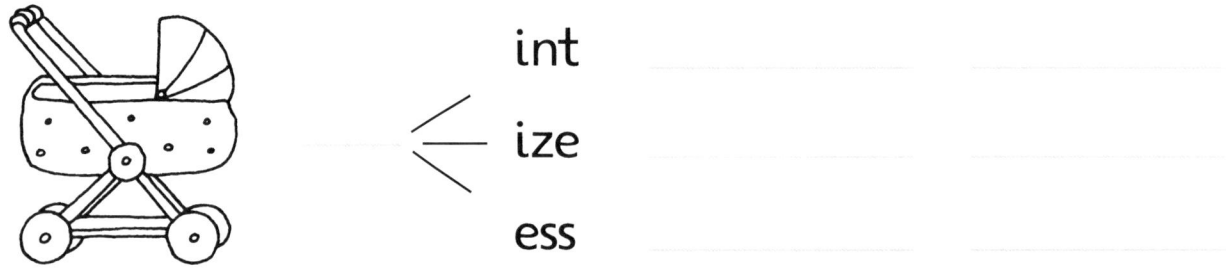

int
ize
ess

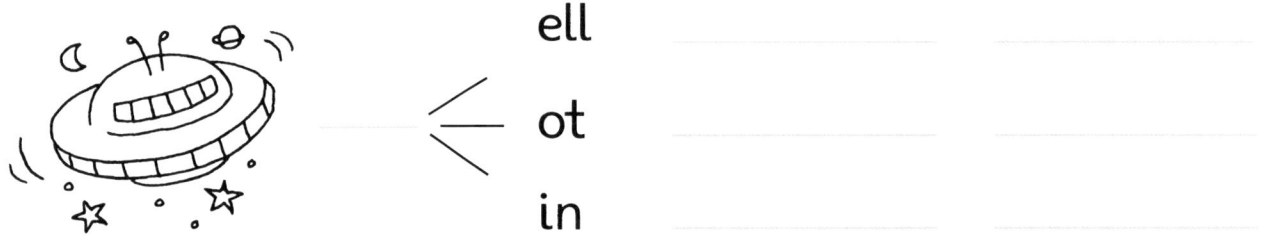

ell
ot
in

ack
ink
ock

Kim and the shape dragon

Skill: Recognizing blends and word-building
Instructions: Write the blend next to the picture. Then use the blend and endings to make the words and write the words twice.

Kim and the computer stories
Stage 8

Name

Sequence the story.

1   One day Kim was playing a spelling game on the computer.

   It was Bleep. 'I can help you to get the mouse working again,' he said.

   Kim saw some little footprints. They were mouse prints.

   She tried to spell the word **sat** but the mouse made **rat**.

   The computer screen went red, then blue, then green and a little face appeared.

   'First we must find out where Mouse lives,' said Bleep.

   Kim and Bleep followed the prints to a little mouse house.

   'Thank you,' said Mouse. 'Now I can get back to work.'

   Kim and Bleep gave Mouse a nice warm drink and some cheese.

Kim and the computer mouse

Skill: Reading for meaning
Instructions: Read all the sentences, then number them in the correct order.

Circle the blend.

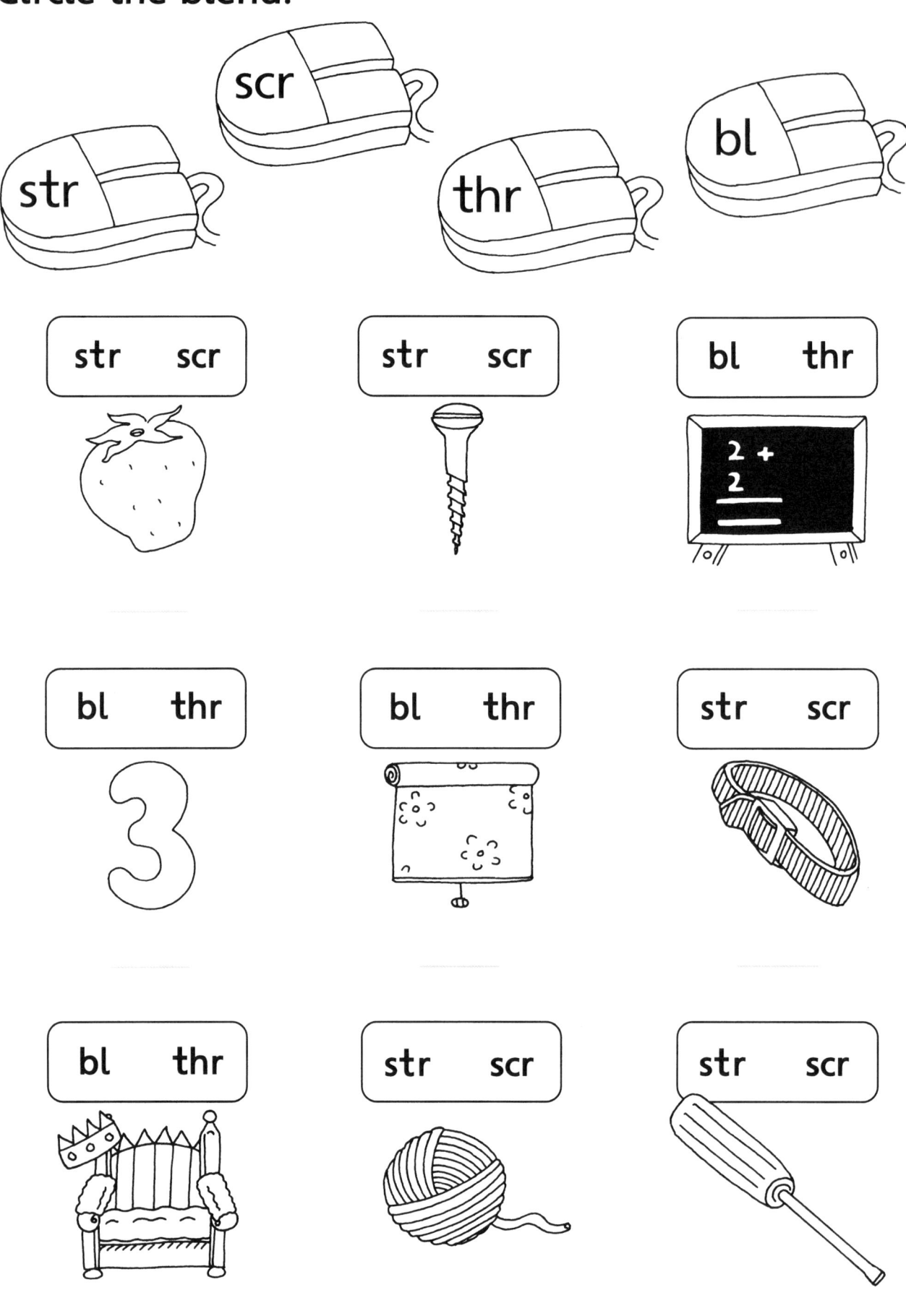

Kim and the computer mouse

Skill: Recognizing blends
Instructions: Circle the correct blend above each picture and then write the blend under the picture.

True or false?

Kim was making up a story about a giant.   true   false

Bleep wanted to see a giant.   true   false

There was no food to eat on the table.   true   false

The giant threw Kim and Bleep down a big hole.   true   false

Kim and Bleep climbed out of the giant's window.   true   false

Kim and Bleep ran across the keyboard.   true   false

The giant jumped on the Delete key and disappeared. true   false

Kim and Bleep jumped on the Delete key.   true   false

Kim was not hungry at the end of the story.   true   false

When Kim got back into the classroom it was time
for lunch.   true   false

Kim and the computer giant

Skill: Story recall and comprehension
Instructions: Read the sentences and decide whether they are true or false. Circle the correct answer. Look back at the story to check your answers.

Match the words.

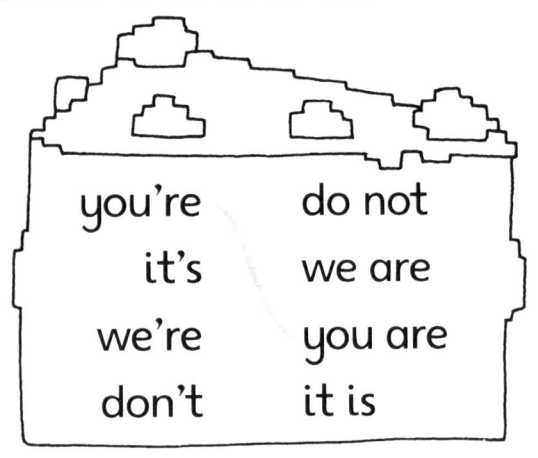

you're — do not
it's — we are
we're — you are
don't — it is

there's — we will
I'm — he is
we'll — there is
he's — I am

Write one word for two words.

you are

Bleep said, 'If _____ hungry, there's lots of food in here.'

do not

'I hope we _____ see your hungry giant,' said Bleep.

It is

'Oh no,' said Bleep. '_____ your hungry giant.'

We are

'Oh no,' said Kim. '_____ in the giant's cooking pot.'

We will

'_____ have to climb up the giant vegetables,' said Bleep.

He is

'Quick,' said Kim. '_____ coming to get us.'

I am

'We have got away from the giant. But now _____ even more hungry,' said Kim.

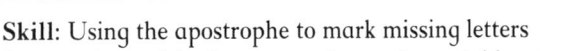

Kim and the computer giant

Skill: Using the apostrophe to mark missing letters
Instructions: Join the contraction to the matching two words. Then write the contractions in the sentences.

My own story

Kim   Bleep   Little Red Riding Hood   Paintbrush

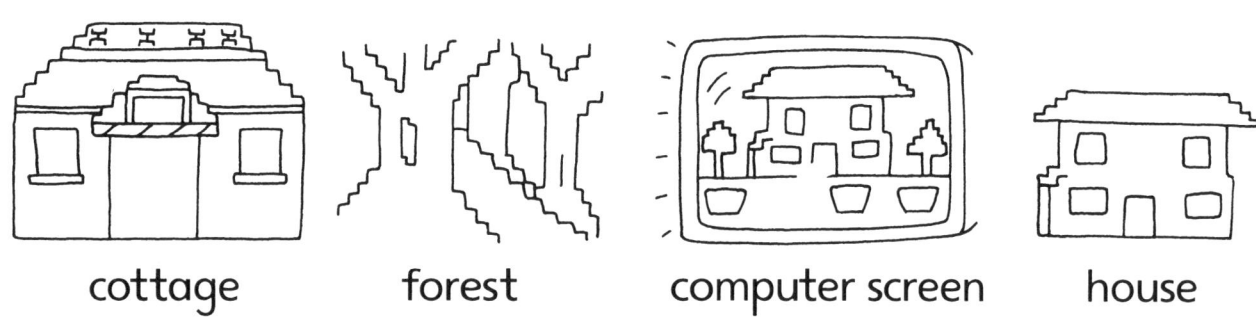

cottage   forest   computer screen   house

Kim and the missing paint pot

Skill: Story writing
Instructions: Choose some characters and an object/setting. Write a new story or re-tell the story of Kim and the missing paint pot.

Answer the questions.

What was Kim making on the computer? (page 2)

Why was Paintbrush cross? (page 5)

What did Cinderella have all over her dress? (page 7)

Who had a beautiful red doll's house? (page 9)

Why had Grandmother taken the red paint? (page 11)

Why did Mrs Morris tell Kim to turn off the computer? (page 15)

Who was painting the roof in Kim's picture? (page 16)

Kim and the missing paint pot

Skill: Comprehension
Instructions: Answer the questions. Look back at the story to help you.

Fill in the gaps.

Kim was playing a shape game on _____ computer.

Bleep said, 'I can help you to _____ the missing triangle.'

Kim and Bleep _____ through the door into a long tunnel.

'The shape dragon has taken all the triangles,' _____ Bleep.

At the back of the cave _____ a dragon.

The dragon had big red triangles _____ his back.

'Please may I _____ one of your triangles?' said Kim.

'I will _____ you my star badge,' said Kim.

So Kim gave the dragon the star badge from _____ jumper.

The dragon gave Kim the little green triangle from the _____ of his tail.

Kim and the shape dragon

Skill: Reading comprehension - cloze
Instructions: Read the sentences carefully and then fill in each gap with a suitable word.

Make the words.

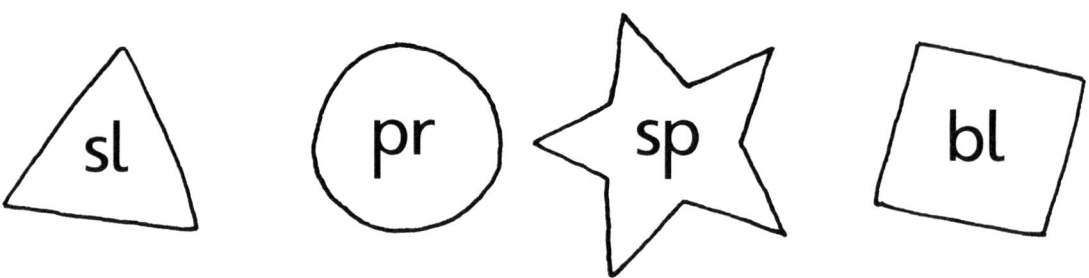

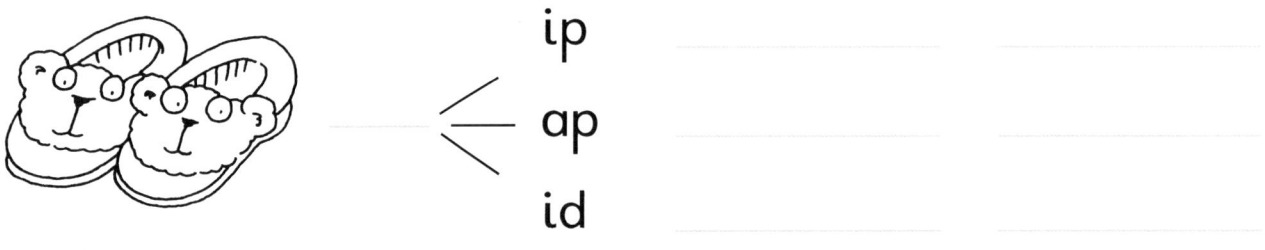

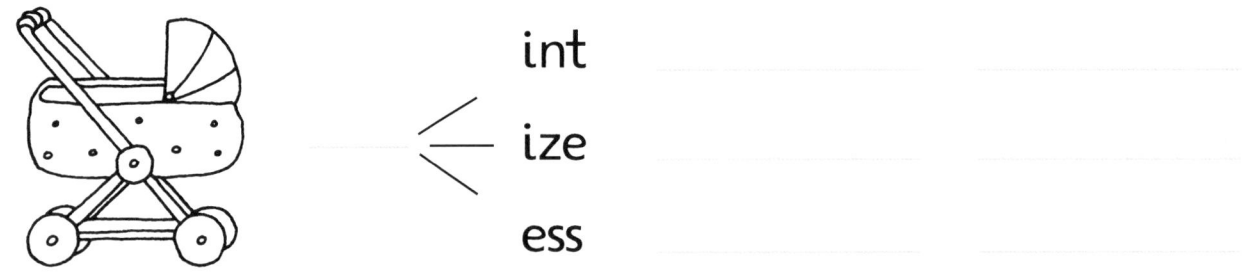

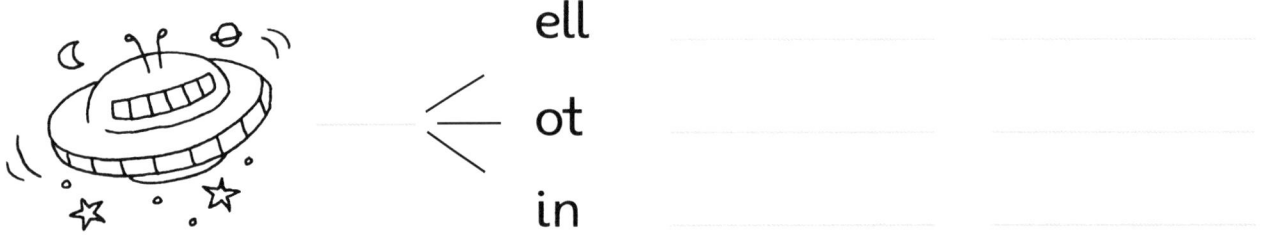

Kim and the shape dragon

Skill: Recognizing blends and word-building
Instructions: Write the blend next to the picture. Then use the blend and endings to make the words and write the words twice.

8

Kim and the computer stories
Stage 8

Name

Sequence the story.

1   One day Kim was playing a spelling game on the computer.

     It was Bleep. 'I can help you to get the mouse working again,' he said.

     Kim saw some little footprints. They were mouse prints.

     She tried to spell the word **sat** but the mouse made **rat**.

     The computer screen went red, then blue, then green and a little face appeared.

     'First we must find out where Mouse lives,' said Bleep.

     Kim and Bleep followed the prints to a little mouse house.

     'Thank you,' said Mouse. 'Now I can get back to work.'

     Kim and Bleep gave Mouse a nice warm drink and some cheese.

Kim and the computer mouse

Skill: Reading for meaning
Instructions: Read all the sentences, then number them in the correct order.

Circle the blend.

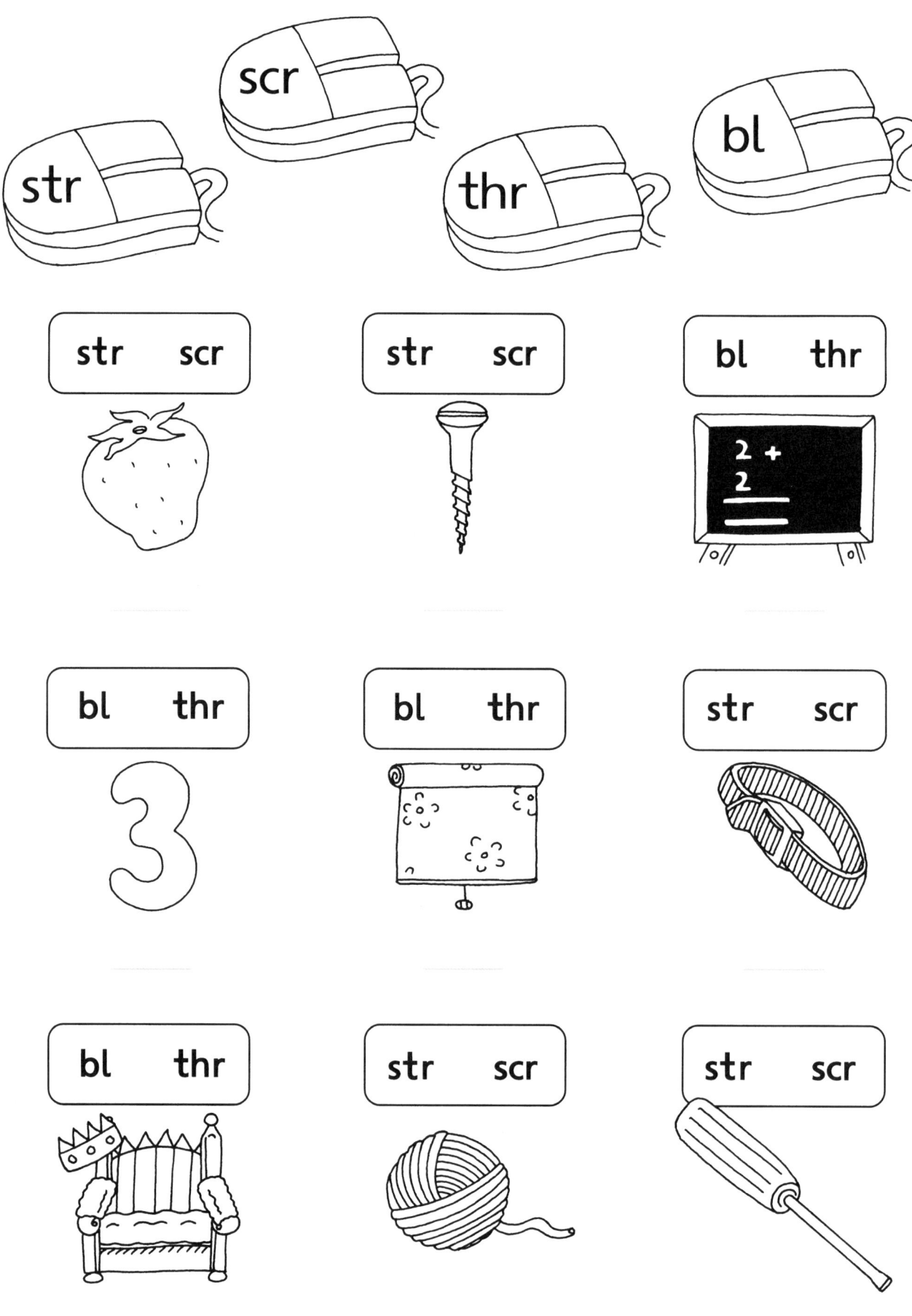

Kim and the computer mouse

Skill: Recognizing blends
Instructions: Circle the correct blend above each picture and then write the blend under the picture.

True or false?

Kim was making up a story about a giant.	true	false
Bleep wanted to see a giant.	true	false
There was no food to eat on the table.	true	false
The giant threw Kim and Bleep down a big hole.	true	false
Kim and Bleep climbed out of the giant's window.	true	false
Kim and Bleep ran across the keyboard.	true	false
The giant jumped on the Delete key and disappeared.	true	false
Kim and Bleep jumped on the Delete key.	true	false
Kim was not hungry at the end of the story.	true	false
When Kim got back into the classroom it was time for lunch.	true	false

Kim and the computer giant

Skill: Story recall and comprehension
Instructions: Read the sentences and decide whether they are true or false. Circle the correct answer. Look back at the story to check your answers.

Match the words.

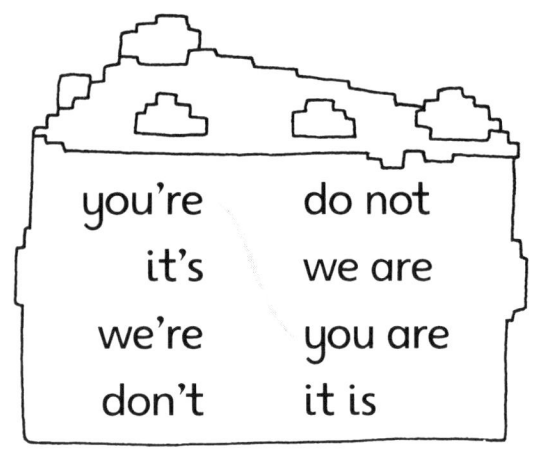

you're — do not
it's — we are
we're — you are
don't — it is

there's — we will
I'm — he is
we'll — there is
he's — I am

Write one word for two words.

you are

Bleep said, 'If _____ hungry, there's lots of food in here.'

do not

'I hope we _____ see your hungry giant,' said Bleep.

It is

'Oh no,' said Bleep. '_____ your hungry giant.'

We are

'Oh no,' said Kim. '_____ in the giant's cooking pot.'

We will

'_____ have to climb up the giant vegetables,' said Bleep.

He is

'Quick,' said Kim. '_____ coming to get us.'

I am

'We have got away from the giant. But now _____ even more hungry,' said Kim.

Kim and the computer giant

Skill: Using the apostrophe to mark missing letters
Instructions: Join the contraction to the matching two words. Then write the contractions in the sentences.

My own story

Kim   Bleep   Little Red Riding Hood   Paintbrush

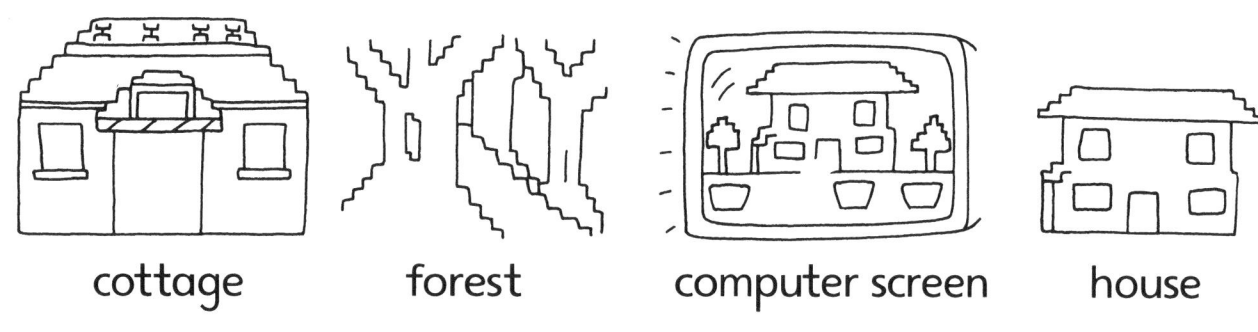

cottage   forest   computer screen   house

Kim and the missing paint pot

Skill: Story writing
Instructions: Choose some characters and an object/setting. Write a new story or re-tell the story of Kim and the missing paint pot.

Answer the questions.

What was Kim making on the computer? (page 2)

Why was Paintbrush cross? (page 5)

What did Cinderella have all over her dress? (page 7)

Who had a beautiful red doll's house? (page 9)

Why had Grandmother taken the red paint? (page 11)

Why did Mrs Morris tell Kim to turn off the computer? (page 15)

Who was painting the roof in Kim's picture? (page 16)

Kim and the missing paint pot

Skill: Comprehension
Instructions: Answer the questions. Look back at the story to help you.

Fill in the gaps.

Kim was playing a shape game on _____ computer.

Bleep said, 'I can help you to _____ the missing triangle.'

Kim and Bleep _____ through the door into a long tunnel.

'The shape dragon has taken all the triangles,' _____ Bleep.

At the back of the cave _____ a dragon.

The dragon had big red triangles _____ his back.

'Please may I _____ one of your triangles?' said Kim.

'I will _____ you my star badge,' said Kim.

So Kim gave the dragon the star badge from _____ jumper.

The dragon gave Kim the little green triangle from the _____ of his tail.

Kim and the shape dragon

Skill: Reading comprehension - cloze
Instructions: Read the sentences carefully and then fill in each gap with a suitable word.

Make the words.

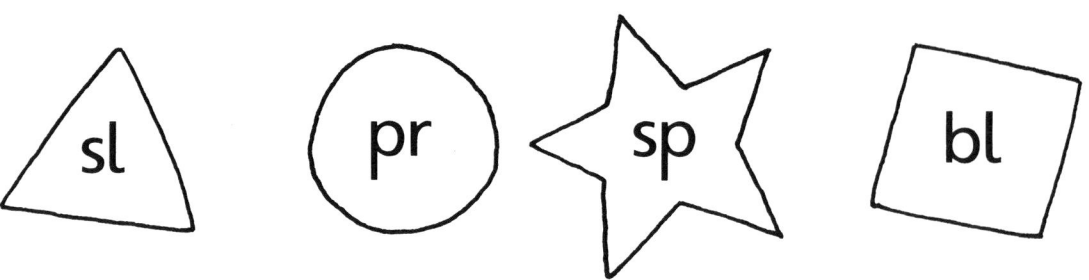

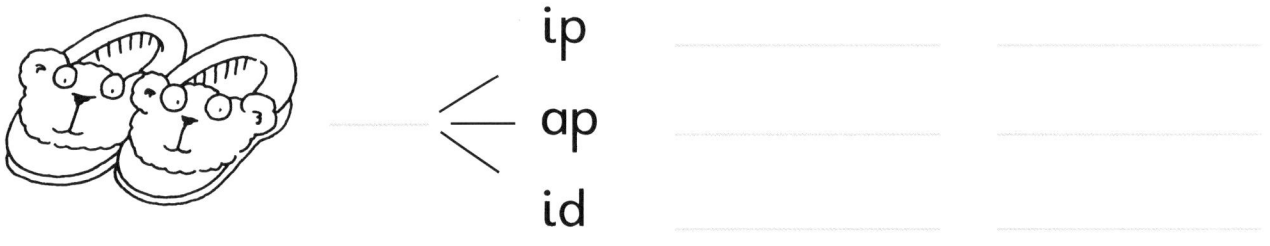

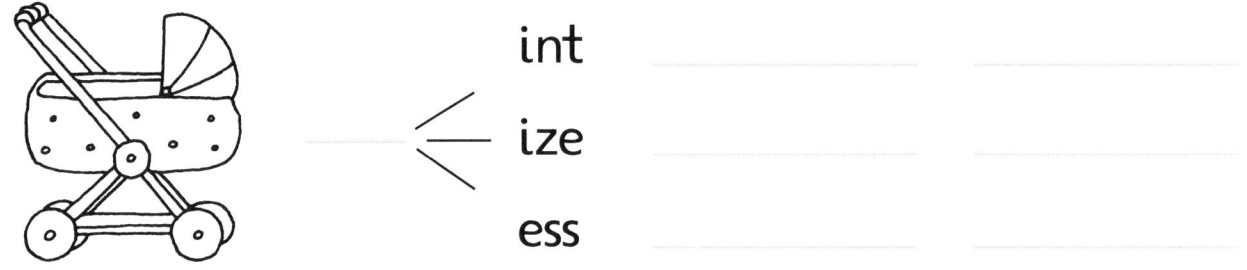

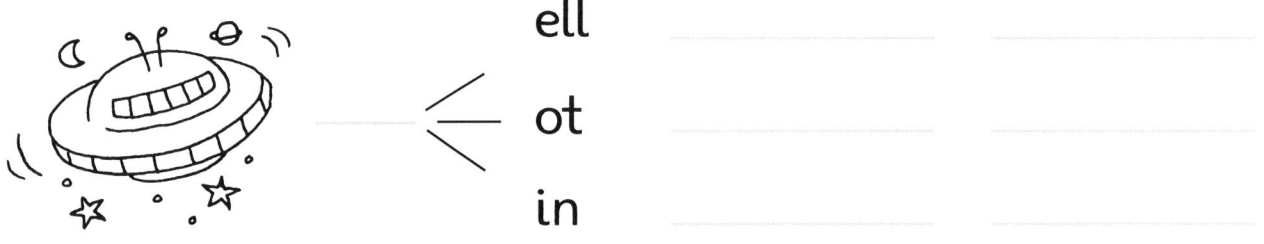

Kim and the shape dragon

Skill: Recognizing blends and word-building
Instructions: Write the blend next to the picture. Then use the blend and endings to make the words and write the words twice.

Kim and the computer stories
Stage 8

Name

Sequence the story.

1   One day Kim was playing a spelling game on the computer.

     It was Bleep. 'I can help you to get the mouse working again,' he said.

     Kim saw some little footprints. They were mouse prints.

     She tried to spell the word **sat** but the mouse made **rat**.

     The computer screen went red, then blue, then green and a little face appeared.

     'First we must find out where Mouse lives,' said Bleep.

     Kim and Bleep followed the prints to a little mouse house.

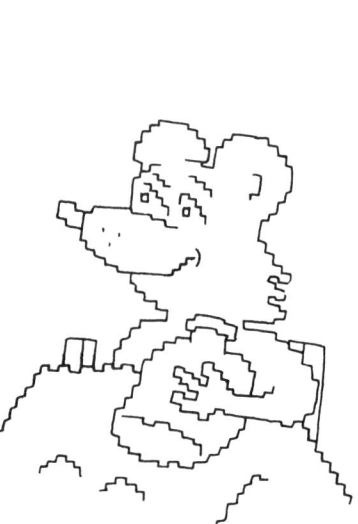

     'Thank you,' said Mouse. 'Now I can get back to work.'

     Kim and Bleep gave Mouse a nice warm drink and some cheese.

Kim and the computer mouse

Skill: Reading for meaning
Instructions: Read all the sentences, then number them in the correct order.

Circle the blend.

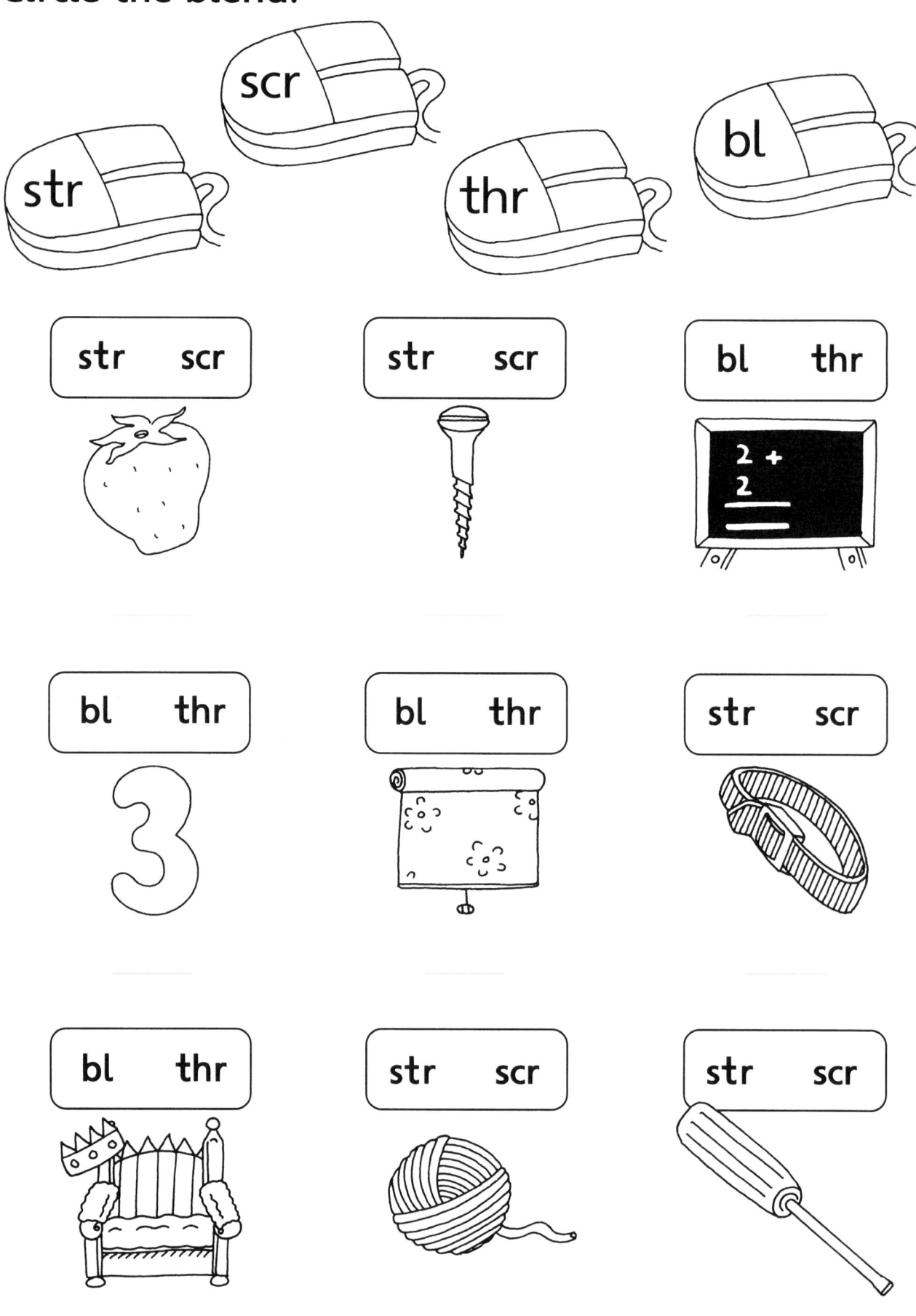

Kim and the computer mouse

Skill: Recognizing blends
Instructions: Circle the correct blend above each picture and then write the blend under the picture.

True or false?

Kim was making up a story about a giant.	true	false
Bleep wanted to see a giant.	true	false
There was no food to eat on the table.	true	false
The giant threw Kim and Bleep down a big hole.	true	false
Kim and Bleep climbed out of the giant's window.	true	false
Kim and Bleep ran across the keyboard.	true	false
The giant jumped on the Delete key and disappeared.	true	false
Kim and Bleep jumped on the Delete key.	true	false
Kim was not hungry at the end of the story.	true	false
When Kim got back into the classroom it was time for lunch.	true	false

Kim and the computer giant

Skill: Story recall and comprehension
Instructions: Read the sentences and decide whether they are true or false. Circle the correct answer. Look back at the story to check your answers.

Match the words.

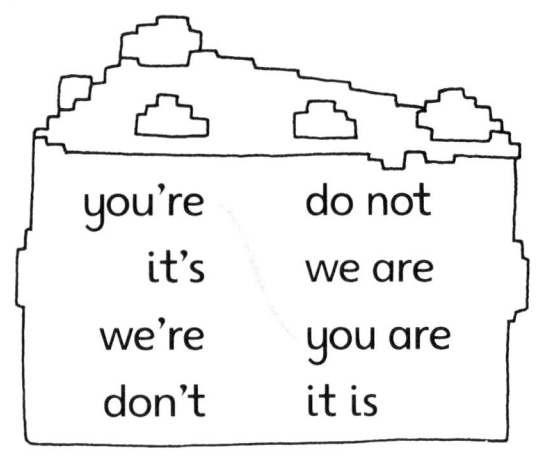

Write one word for two words.

you are

Bleep said, 'If _____ hungry, there's lots of food in here.'

do not

'I hope we _____ see your hungry giant,' said Bleep.

It is

'Oh no,' said Bleep. '_____ your hungry giant.'

We are

'Oh no,' said Kim. '_____ in the giant's cooking pot.'

We will

'_____ have to climb up the giant vegetables,' said Bleep.

He is

'Quick,' said Kim. '_____ coming to get us.'

I am

'We have got away from the giant. But now _____ even more hungry,' said Kim.

Kim and the computer giant

Skill: Using the apostrophe to mark missing letters
Instructions: Join the contraction to the matching two words. Then write the contractions in the sentences.

My own story

Kim   Bleep   Little Red Riding Hood   Paintbrush

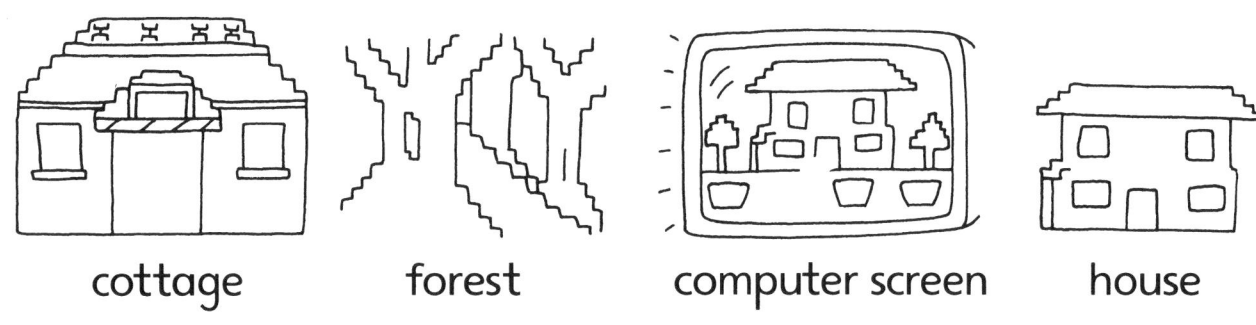

cottage   forest   computer screen   house

Kim and the missing paint pot

Skill: Story writing
Instructions: Choose some characters and an object/setting. Write a new story or re-tell the story of Kim and the missing paint pot.

Answer the questions.

What was Kim making on the computer? (page 2)

Why was Paintbrush cross? (page 5)

What did Cinderella have all over her dress? (page 7)

Who had a beautiful red doll's house? (page 9)

Why had Grandmother taken the red paint? (page 11)

Why did Mrs Morris tell Kim to turn off the computer? (page 15)

Who was painting the roof in Kim's picture? (page 16)

Kim and the missing paint pot

Skill: Comprehension
Instructions: Answer the questions. Look back at the story to help you.

Fill in the gaps.

Kim was playing a shape game on _____ computer.

Bleep said, 'I can help you to _____ the missing triangle.'

Kim and Bleep _____ through the door into a long tunnel.

'The shape dragon has taken all the triangles,' _____ Bleep.

At the back of the cave _____ a dragon.

The dragon had big red triangles _____ his back.

'Please may I _____ one of your triangles?' said Kim.

'I will _____ you my star badge,' said Kim.

So Kim gave the dragon the star badge from _____ jumper.

The dragon gave Kim the little green triangle from the _____ of his tail.

Kim and the shape dragon

Skill: Reading comprehension - cloze
Instructions: Read the sentences carefully and then fill in each gap with a suitable word.

Make the words.

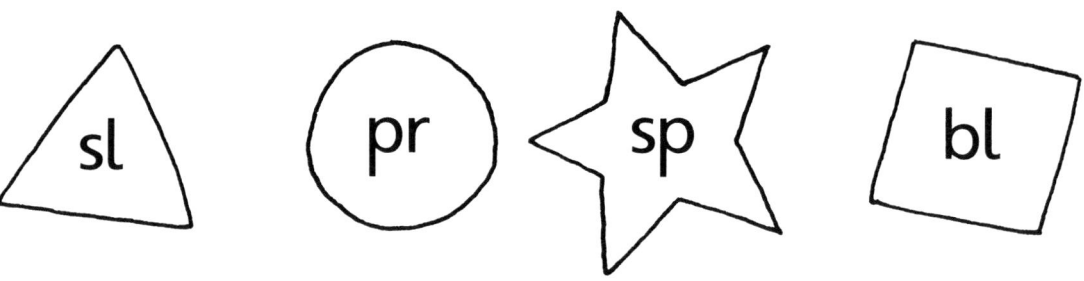

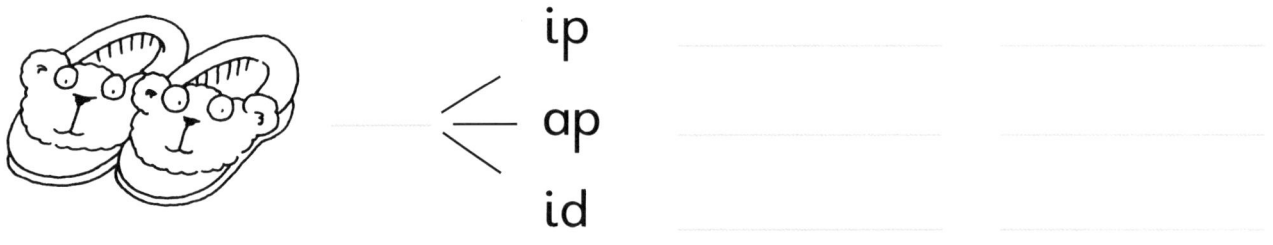

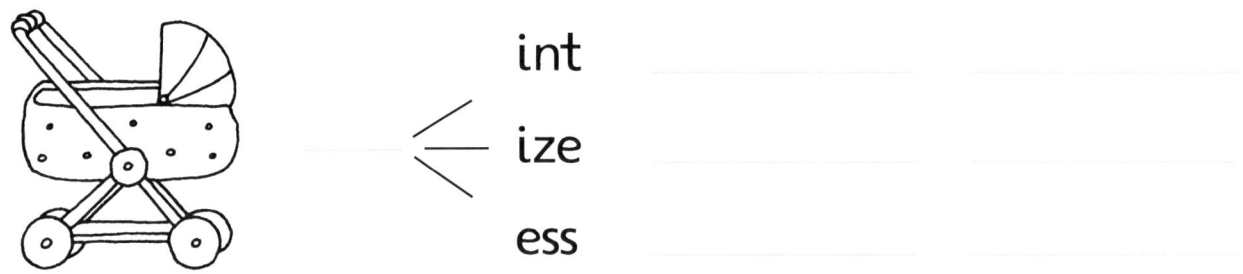

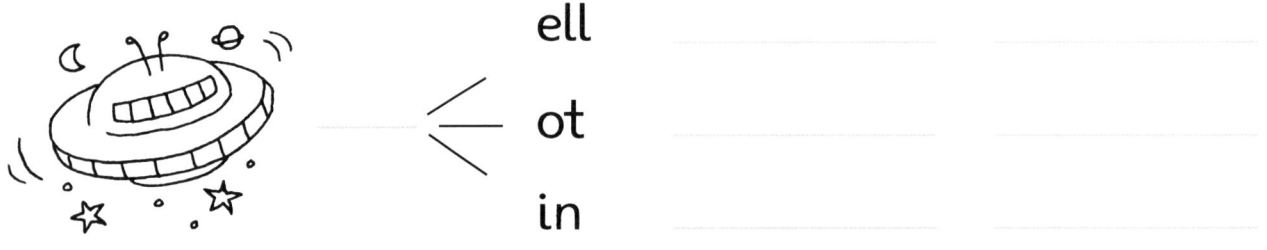

Kim and the shape dragon

Skill: Recognizing blends and word-building
Instructions: Write the blend next to the picture. Then use the blend and endings to make the words and write the words twice.

Name

Sequence the story.

Kim and the computer stories
Stage 8

1   One day Kim was playing a spelling game on the computer.

It was Bleep. 'I can help you to get the mouse working again,' he said.

Kim saw some little footprints. They were mouse prints.

She tried to spell the word **sat** but the mouse made **rat**.

The computer screen went red, then blue, then green and a little face appeared.

'First we must find out where Mouse lives,' said Bleep.

Kim and Bleep followed the prints to a little mouse house.

'Thank you,' said Mouse. 'Now I can get back to work.'

Kim and Bleep gave Mouse a nice warm drink and some cheese.

Kim and the computer mouse

Skill: Reading for meaning
Instructions: Read all the sentences, then number them in the correct order.

Circle the blend.

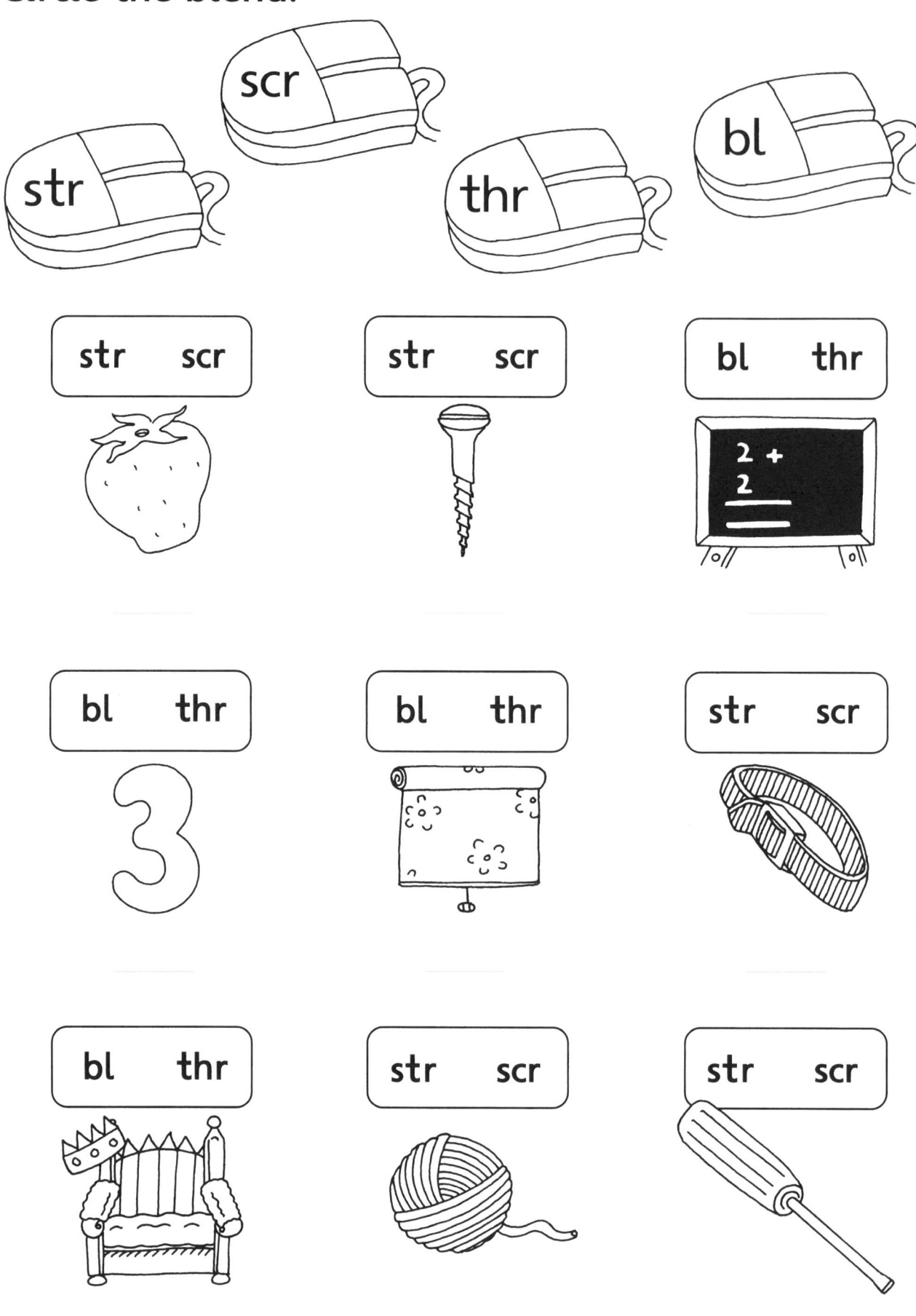

Kim and the computer mouse

Skill: Recognizing blends
Instructions: Circle the correct blend above each picture and then write the blend under the picture.

True or false?

Kim was making up a story about a giant.	true	false
Bleep wanted to see a giant.	true	false
There was no food to eat on the table.	true	false
The giant threw Kim and Bleep down a big hole.	true	false
Kim and Bleep climbed out of the giant's window.	true	false
Kim and Bleep ran across the keyboard.	true	false
The giant jumped on the Delete key and disappeared.	true	false
Kim and Bleep jumped on the Delete key.	true	false
Kim was not hungry at the end of the story.	true	false
When Kim got back into the classroom it was time for lunch.	true	false

Kim and the computer giant

Skill: Story recall and comprehension
Instructions: Read the sentences and decide whether they are true or false. Circle the correct answer. Look back at the story to check your answers.

Match the words.

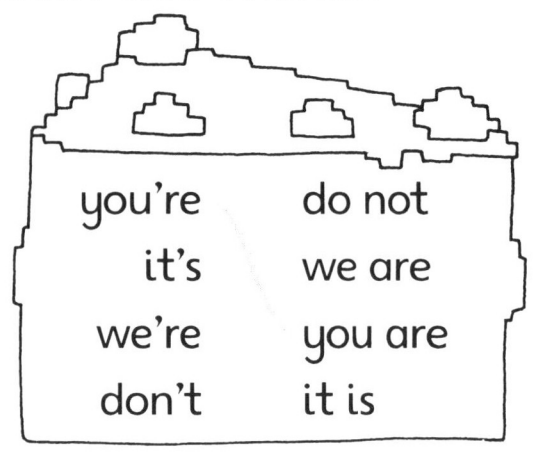

you're — do not
it's — we are
we're — you are
don't — it is

there's — we will
I'm — he is
we'll — there is
he's — I am

Write one word for two words.

you are

Bleep said, 'If _____ hungry, there's lots of food in here.'

do not

'I hope we _____ see your hungry giant,' said Bleep.

It is

'Oh no,' said Bleep. '_____ your hungry giant.'

We are

'Oh no,' said Kim. '_____ in the giant's cooking pot.'

We will

'_____ have to climb up the giant vegetables,' said Bleep.

He is

'Quick,' said Kim. '_____ coming to get us.'

I am

'We have got away from the giant. But now _____ even more hungry,' said Kim.

Kim and the computer giant

Skill: Using the apostrophe to mark missing letters
Instructions: Join the contraction to the matching two words. Then write the contractions in the sentences.

My own story

Kim   Bleep   Little Red Riding Hood   Paintbrush

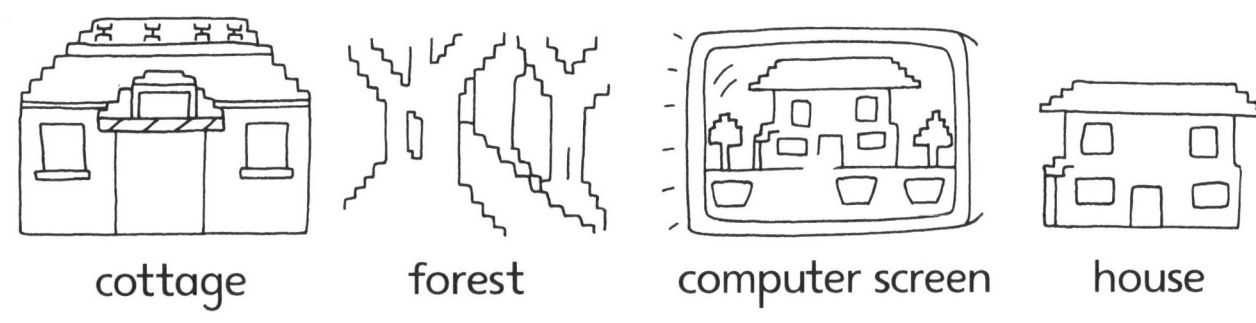

cottage   forest   computer screen   house

Kim and the missing paint pot

Skill: Story writing
Instructions: Choose some characters and an object/setting. Write a new story or re-tell the story of Kim and the missing paint pot.

Answer the questions.

What was Kim making on the computer? (page 2)

Why was Paintbrush cross? (page 5)

What did Cinderella have all over her dress? (page 7)

Who had a beautiful red doll's house? (page 9)

Why had Grandmother taken the red paint? (page 11)

Why did Mrs Morris tell Kim to turn off the computer? (page 15)

Who was painting the roof in Kim's picture? (page 16)

Kim and the missing paint pot

Skill: Comprehension
Instructions: Answer the questions. Look back at the story to help you.

Fill in the gaps.

Kim was playing a shape game on _____ computer.

Bleep said, 'I can help you to _____ the missing triangle.'

Kim and Bleep _____ through the door into a long tunnel.

'The shape dragon has taken all the triangles,' _____ Bleep.

At the back of the cave _____ a dragon.

The dragon had big red triangles _____ his back.

'Please may I _____ one of your triangles?' said Kim.

'I will _____ you my star badge,' said Kim.

So Kim gave the dragon the star badge from _____ jumper.

The dragon gave Kim the little green triangle from the _____ of his tail.

Kim and the shape dragon

Skill: Reading comprehension - cloze
Instructions: Read the sentences carefully and then fill in each gap with a suitable word.

Make the words.

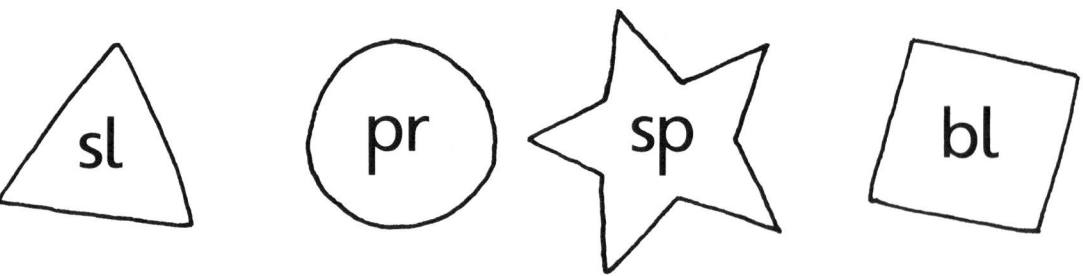

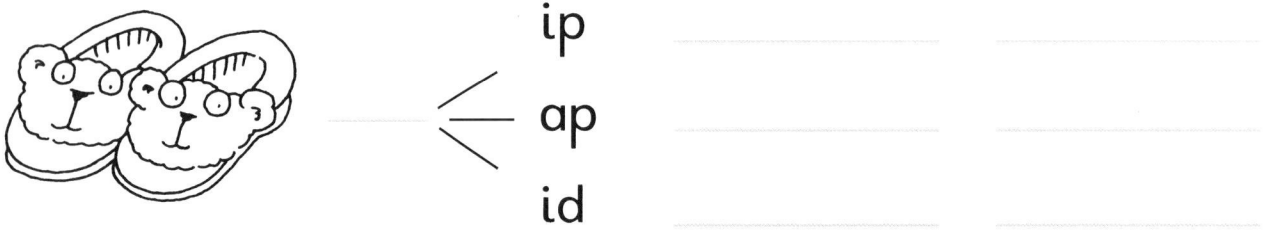

ip
ap
id

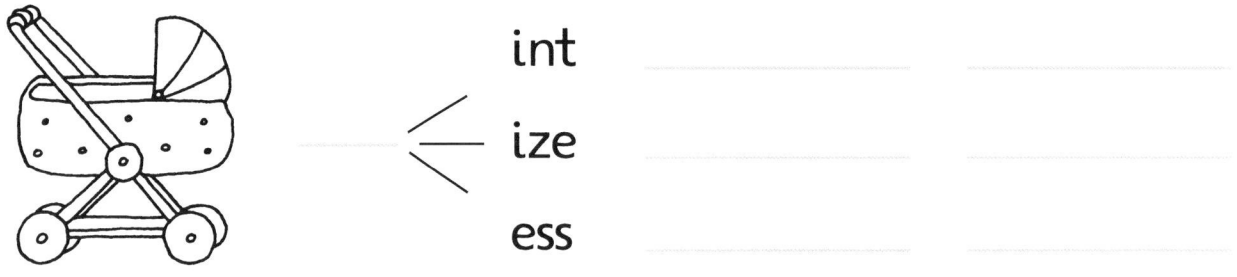

int
ize
ess

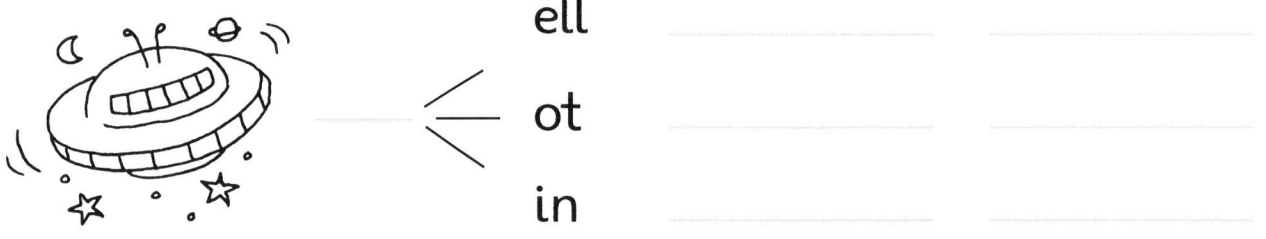

ell
ot
in

ack
ink
ock

Kim and the shape dragon

Skill: Recognizing blends and word-building
Instructions: Write the blend next to the picture. Then use the blend and endings to make the words and write the words twice.